REGENERATION

These Studies are designed to inform the mature student—the undergraduate upperclassman and the beginning graduate student—of the outstanding advances made in various areas of modern biology. The books will not be treatises but rather will briefly summarize significant information in a given field and interpret it in terms of our current knowledge of the rapidly expanding research findings within the life sciences. Also it is hoped that the Studies will be of interest to teachers and research workers.

BIOLOGY STUDIES ←

Elizabeth D. Hay
Harvard Medical School
Boston, Massachusetts

REGENERATION

Holt, Rinehart
and Winston
New York, Chicago,
San Francisco,
Toronto, London

This volume is affectionately dedicated to

MERYL AND FLORENCE ROSE

who stimulated my interest in regeneration,

and to

OSCAR SCHOTTÉ

who stimulated their interest in regeneration,

in appreciation of the friendship

and help they have so generously given me

over the years.

preface ▶▶▶▶▶▶

The present book is written so much from the point of view of the cytologist that I might well have included the term "cyto-differentiation" in the title. The subject, however, is definitely regeneration and the book aims to introduce the reader to all aspects of the topic in as concise a manner as possible. The organization is vertical—that is to say, the animal phyla are considered separately and in phylogenetic order. In this way, differences among the animals are emphasized and quick reference to a single group is expedited. Phylogenetic charts are included to further this end. The illustrations are numerous and serve to expand many points that are often mentioned only too briefly in the text. Judging from the past comments of graduate students, access to illustrations of such diverse origin in one book should in itself justify this publication.

The first chapter deals with invertebrate regeneration and contains a discussion of asexual reproduction as well. The second chapter emphasizes the cytology of amphibian limb regeneration, lens regeneration, and distribution of regenerative capacities among vertebrates. The third chapter covers mammalian physiological and reparative regeneration in sufficient depth to be of use to medical students, anatomists, and pathologists. The fourth chapter is a synopsis of studies on the fine structure of regeneration cells and includes a re-evaluation of the "reserve cell" problem. The concepts of differentiation, dedifferentiation, and "totipotency" are re-examined in the light of recent experiments on embryos and regenerating systems.

I wish to thank Mary J. Powers, whose expert editorial and secretarial help made completion of the manuscript possible. I am grateful to S. Meryl Rose, Tulane University, to Sidney B. Simpson, Jr., Western Reserve University, to J. David Deck,

University of Virginia, and to S. James Adelstein, Anita Hoffer, and Margaret Byers, Harvard Medical School for their assistance in reading and revising the manuscript; to a number of authors for the use of their published figures; to Sylvia Colard Keene for her skill in drawing the phylogenetic charts; and to Jean-Paul Revel for allowing me to use figures from our unpublished joint work. The United States Public Health Service supported my published research and the studies of *Perophera* and *Dugesia* reported here for the first time.

The bibliography is comprehensive, but in order to keep it within limits I have often referred to reviews at the expense of individual authors, to whom I apologize in advance.

E.D.H.

Boston, Massachusetts
April 1966

contents

 **REGENERATION**

chapter one

Invertebrate Regeneration and Reproduction

PHYLOGENETIC RELATIONS

The degree to which the life of the individual organism, as opposed to the species, is immortal is reflected in the balance between asexual reproduction and regeneration on the one hand, and sexual reproduction, on the other. We shall have an opportunity in this chapter to examine some rather remarkable regenerative phenomena in the so-called lower animals. In many cases, these phenomena are closely related to the devices for asexual reproduction that have evolved in the various groups. We will, therefore, review briefly the processes of asexual reproduction before taking up the processes of regeneration per se. Let us first consider the general phylogenetic relationships among our invertebrate relatives, so that we can view the varied types of reproduction in relation to the complexity of the animals and their position on the phylogenetic tree.

It is convenient to subdivide the animals into two groups, the acoelomate or primitive phyla (Fig. 1-1), and the more advanced phyla consisting of animals which possess true coelomic cavities and more elaborate organ systems (Fig. 1-2). The protozoa, sponges, coelenterates, and flatworms comprise the major phyla of so-called primitive animals. As a general rule, it is fair to say that capacities for regeneration and asexual reproduction are most developed in the primitive animals, but as we shall see, there are marked exceptions to this rule.

Although composed of only one "cell," the protozoa complex intracellular differentiations and is able to live in of environments, ranging from the blood of man (the ma

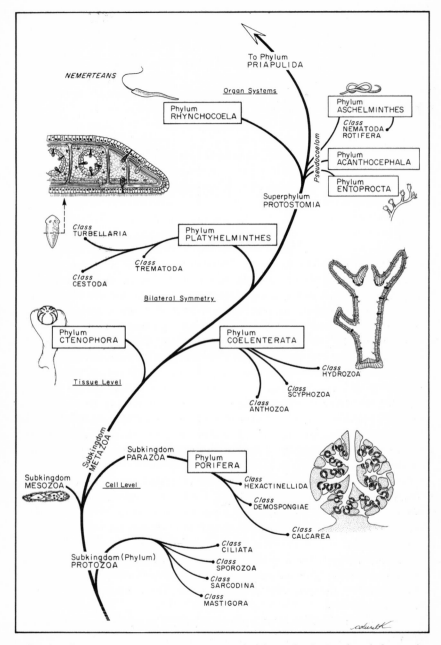

Fig. 1-1. Phylogeny of the acoelomate or primitive animals. In the phylogenetic charts depicted in Figs. 1-1 and 1-2, the animals are arranged as suggested by L. Cockrum and W. J. McCauley, *Zoology*, Philadelphia, W. B. Saunders Co.,

site) to fresh water ponds and salt water seas. We generally speak of four classes (ciliates, sporozoans, rhizopods, and flagellates) within the phylum of protozoans. Certain flagellates, such as *Volvox*, form multicellular colonies of closely associated individuals.

The sponges, which probably derived from such colonial protozoans, are multicellular animals but are classified as parazoa rather than true metazoa because they have not achieved a tissue level of organization. Coordinating mechanisms among the cells are not well developed. The epidermis is a simple epithelium continuous, at intervals, with the lining cells of the sponge pores. The cells of the inner epithelium (choanocytes) contain flagella. Between these two epithelial layers, there is a gelatinous matrix or "mesenchyme" in which wandering "undifferentiated" cells (archaeocytes), matrix-secreting cells, and various spicules occur (Fig. 1-1).

Coelenterates and members of the related phylum, Ctenophora, can be considered true metazoa because they show organized activity and probably contain nerve cells within the epidermis in most cases. The body is made up of two layers of contractile epithelia, and the inner layer lines a gastrovascular cavity (Fig. 1-1). The primitive mesoderm between the two epithelial layers is a gelatinous "mesogloea," best developed in jellyfish (scyphozoans) and in ctenophores.

Flatworms are said to have reached the organ level of organization. They have a well-developed mesoderm, muscles, and nerve cords, and they exhibit primitive kidneys and genital organs. Like coelenterates and ctenophores, however, they have a gastrovascular cavity rather than a true gut. The closely related, but more advanced, ribbon worms (nemerteans) are said to have arrived at the organ system level (Fig. 1-1). They have an extendible proboscis for catching food, a true gut, and a closed circulation consisting of dorsal and lateral blood vessels that are embedded in the mesoderm.

Although several "side-branch" phyla of primitive worms develop a pseudocoelom, a true coelom first appears in relatives of the flatworms (Priapulida) said to be on the "main line" of the evolution leading to the higher animals (Fig. 1-2). A true coelom has its own epithelial lining. It develops as a split in a block of mesoderm (protostomes) or as a series of pouches off the endoderm (deuterostomes). The major coelomate phyla of interest here are

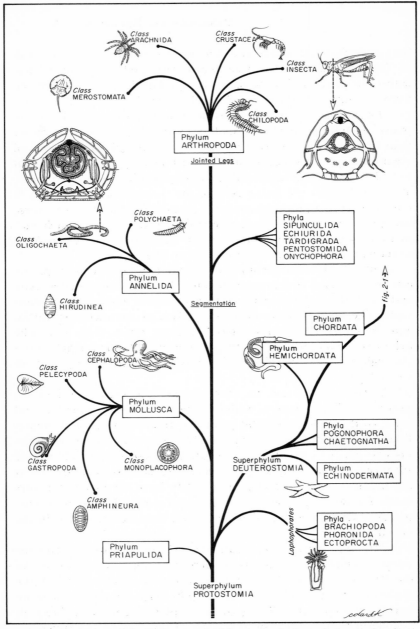

Fig. 1-2. Phylogeny of the coelomate or higher animals. Several classes of arthropods are omitted.

4

the annelids and arthropods which, like the primitive worms, are classified as protostomes (the mouth develops from the blastopore of the embryo); and the echinoderms and chordates, which comprise the main phyla of a side branch known as deuterostomes (animals whose mouth develops at a pole opposite the blastopore). The salient features of their anatomy (Fig. 1-2) will be discussed in more detail when the individual phyla are considered.

ASEXUAL REPRODUCTION

Reproduction in the vertebrates (Fig. 2-1) is exclusively sexual. Male and female gametes are always produced. Regeneration contributes to reproduction only insofar as it helps to maintain the individual; it never produces a new and separate animal. Among the invertebrates, this is certainly not the rule. Almost all of the animals have a sexual cycle, but a variety of modes of asexual reproduction have evolved as well, even in some of our close chordate relatives. Needless to say, regenerative capacities are excellent in animals which are capable of reproducing themselves asexually from somatic cells. There are three principal modes of asexual reproduction: (1) fission, (2) gemmule formation (rare), and (3) budding.

In many protozoans, especially the classes Sarcodina (for example, *Amoeba*) and Mastigora (flagellates), binary fission is the only mode of reproduction. The ciliate *Stentor,* which has been studied extensively in regeneration experiments, provides a good example of binary fission (Fig. 1-3). The animal has a band of cilia around the anterior (adoral) end that carries food into the buccal pouch and gullet. The adoral zone (az, Fig. 1-3) and a single contractile vacuole are reproduced before fission occurs. The macronucleus divides by direct constriction (m, Fig. 1-3) and the micronuclei typical of the ciliates divide by mitosis. Other protozoans have a single nucleus per cell which exhibits conventional mitosis during fission. Certain ciliates (*Paramecium*) have both an asexual mode of reproduction (fission) and a sexual method (conjugation). In the latter case, specific mating types join to exchange genetic materials contained in the many micronuclei. The sporozoans and certain colonial flagellates (*Volvox*) produce true gametes and *Volvox* is said to reproduce by budding as well.

The sponges reproduce by budding and they also form gametes.

In addition, a rather unique reproductive process, involving gemmules, has evolved. The gemmule is an enclosed receptacle containing "totipotent" somatic cells (archaeocytes). Should the parent die in an adverse season, the gemmule survives. Later, when conditions are favorable, the cells crawl out, aggregate around the shell, and form a new sponge. The cells of sponges also exhibit great ability to reaggregate into a complete individual after mechanical or chemical dissociation of the component cells. This laboratory phenomenon, which usually is classified as regeneration, probably is related to the excellent capacity of the cells to aggregate after emerging from the gemmule.

In the metazoa proper, fission and budding occur to some extent in most of the phyla, but gemmule formation is rare (occurring only in Ectoprocta). Fission, or formation of a new individual by splitting off part of the maternal organism, is common in coelenterates and worms, and also is seen in higher forms such as echinoderms (for example, in brittle stars) and tunicates (the sea squirts). Fission, and the related process called strobilation, usually involves transverse division, accomplished by ingrowth of the epidermis (see Berrill, 1961; Balinsky, 1965). Budding, that is, formation of a new individual from a small outgrowth off the parent, is particularly well developed in the primitive coelenterate, on the one hand, and the more complex chordate, the tunicate, on the other. Both these groups also produce gametes, frequently from the same area of the body that produces buds (Lenhoff and Loomis, 1961; Berrill, 1961).

The origin of the bud of the common fresh-water medusa of southern Africa has been well documented by Bouillon (Fig. 1-4). There are no interstitial cells in the region where budding takes place. The first step in the development of a bud on the medusa is an outgrowth of epidermis and endodermis. The cytoplasm of the epithelial cells in the apical part of the bud becomes basophilic in its staining reaction and the cells lose their vacuoles. The partially dedifferentiated ectodermal cells proliferate to form a plate which subsequently thickens to produce a nodule, the entocodon (Fig. 1-4, C). The entocodon detaches from the base of the apical epidermis and develops a lumen, the subumbrellar cavity. The tentacular cavity forms in the outermost epidermis, now called the tentacular ectoderm (Fig. 1-4, D). The entocodon seems to stimulate proliferation in adjacent endodermal cells and these cells give rise to mar-

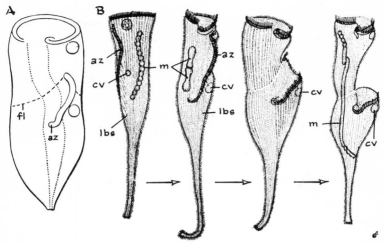

Fig. 1-3. Fission in the ciliate protozoan, *Stentor*. (*A*) Diagram to show the location of the future fission line (fl). The animal depicted has begun to develop the new adoral zone (az) and contractile vacuole that will be part of the offspring. The adoral region of the parent animal appears at the top of the diagram. (*B*) Four stages of fission, showing reconstitution of typical form in each new individual. The cone-shaped *Stentor* is attached to the substratum by its narrow disclike foot. In the first stage shown, the new adoral zone (az) and contractile vacuole (cv) have appeared. The pigmented longitudinal stripes and bands of cilia are reproduced from the so-called left boundary stripe (lbs) near the foot of the animal. The macronucleus (m) contracts to a single fusion mass and the micronuclei (not shown) divide in the next stage of fission. Then the macronucleus splits in two and renodulates. A new foot will form on the upper animal as the transverse fission proceeds to completion. (After H. P. Johnson (1893) and others, from *Growth, Development, and Pattern,* by N. J. Berrill. Copyright by W. H. Freeman and Company, 1961.)

ginal and radial canals and gastrovascular tract. Epidermal cells in the same region of the animal that gives rise to buds in winter have the capacity to transform into gametes in spring. So-called reserve cells or interstitial cells that lie within the epidermis of the polyp, *Hydra,* seem to multiply during budding and are thought to give rise to the new cells (Fig. 1-5). Interstitial cells seem to be involved in replacement of cnidoblasts (cells that produce the stinging capsules) in all coelenterates. Whether or not they are essential for

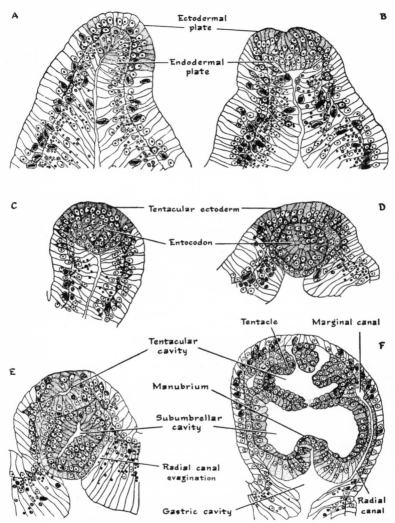

Fig. 1-4. Origin of bud during asexual reproduction of the fresh-water medusa, *Limnocnida*. In this coelenterate, buds may form from the manubrium of the medusa or from the stem of the minute, sessile hydroid. There are no interstitial cells in the region where budding takes place. The apical epidermis proliferates to form a nodule, the entocodon, which gives rise to the subumbrellar cavity and influences the development of the other structures in the bud (see text). (After J. Bouillon, from *Growth, Development, and Pattern,* by N. J. Berrill. Copyright by W. H. Freeman and Company, 1961.)

8

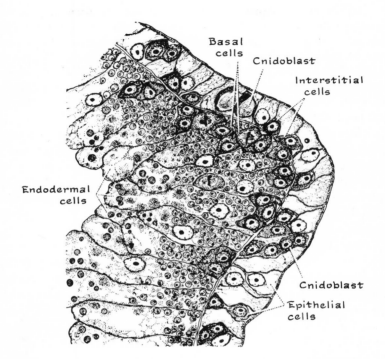

Fig. 1-5. Origin of bud during asexual reproduction of the hydrozoan, *Hydra viridis*. This coelenterate, which occurs only in the form of a polyp, is characterized by abundant interstitial cells. The endodermal cells of *Hydra viridis* contains inclusions of algae that are responsible for the green color of the animal. At the beginning of bud formation, a growth zone appears in the endodermis. The area can be recognized by the multiplication of the green chlorellae which characterize the cells. Ectodermal growth then ensues. The basophilic interstitial cells proliferate and differentiate into cnidoblasts near the margin of the bud. In other regions they form epidermal (epitheliomuscular) cells. Interstitial cells from the ectoderm seemingly enter the endodermis and serve as a source of new cells there also. During sexual reproduction in *Hydra viridis,* interstitial cells seem to give rise to the gametes. Asexual budding and gamete formation are mutually exclusive processes. Such factors as temperature and carbon dioxide tension decide which one will predominate. (After P. Brien, from *Growth, Development, and Pattern,* by N. J. Berrill. Copyright by W. H. Freeman and Company, 1961.)

asexual reproduction in hydrozoans is a debatable matter, however. Their possible role in regeneration is discussed on pages 16–18 and again in Chapter Four.

In the colonial tunicates, new buds usually form on the connecting tube or stolon. In noncolonial forms, they develop from the zooid (Fig. 1-6). Budding in *Botryllus* is initiated by a small disk of thickened atrial epithelium (Fig. 1-6, B), which plays the major role in subsequent morphogenesis. The atrial disk becomes a vesicle which produces the definitive organ fields by infoldings of its walls. The epidermis forms in continuity with old epidermis and later will separate the bud from the parent.

New gametes originate from atrial epithelium. They are segregated out at a very early stage of development as is also the case in chordate embryos developing from zygotes. In other tunicates, the tissues that play the important role in bud formation may be the epicardium of the zooid or the mesodermal septum of the stolon. The subject will be considered in more detail at the end of the chapter.

The regenerative processes which occur in the primitive animals (Fig. 1-7) and in the segmented worms and tunicates (Fig. 1-6) are closely related to the processes of asexual reproduction. Indeed, there is no reason to believe that the actual mechanisms of growth are any different in the two cases. The term "reconstitution" often is used to refer to all regenerative processes in the invertebrates and vertebrates (Child, 1941). Reconstitution may be subdivided into: (1) regeneration by outgrowth of new tissue from the wound surface (called epimorphosis by Morgan, 1901); (2) reorganization or remodeling of internal parts (morphallaxis). These distinctions are not very useful today because they do not describe the origin of the regenerate in a satisfactory manner. For example, regeneration of the amphibian limb is said to be an epimorphic process. Yet, there is a striking internal remodeling of the old stump before "outgrowth" begins. The entire blastema of the amphibian limb arises at the expense of the formed tissues which give rise to the regeneration cells. Sometimes the presence or absence of mitotic activity is used to distinguish between epimorphosis and morphallaxis, but studies of cell division in invertebrate regeneration are too incomplete to justify the classification on this basis.

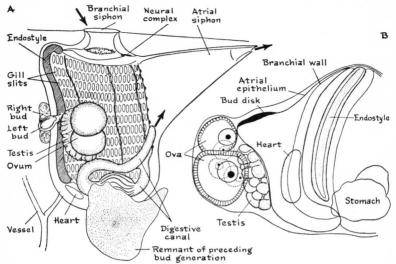

Fig. 1-6. Modes of asexual and sexual reproduction in a tunicate, *Botryllus*. (*A*) The mature gametes and developing buds are depicted in a mature zooid. (*B*) A developing bud is shown at higher magnification. The gametes and buds both arise from atrial epithelium. The timing sequence of development is remarkable. First the atrial epithelium thickens to form a bud disc which evaginates as a hemisphere covered by epidermis. The gametes are segregated at this early stage. The atrial vesicle then forms the branchial and peribranchial compartments, digestive tube, and heart of the young bud, the heart begins to beat, and the bud disc of the next generation appears (*B*). When the zooid attains functional maturity with open siphons (*A*), the gonads also reach maturity, and fertilization occurs. The embryo develops into a free-swimming larva in the peribranchial cavity of the hermaphrodite zooid. In the meantime, the next generation of buds matures and now the parent zooid undergoes dissolution, leaving behind its sexual and asexual offspring to repeat the cycle. The short-lived adult is merely a brief stage in a precise cycle of physiological regeneration which is occurring continuously in *Botryllus*. (From *Growth, Development, and Pattern,* by N. J. Berrill. Copyright by W. H. Freeman and Company, 1961.)

REGENERATION IN PROTOZOA

Regeneration in protozoa is an interesting case in point. The animal is unicellular and regeneration must involve reorganization and remodeling of internal parts, but could conceivably occur without mitosis if there were no nuclear injury. Lund (1917) de-

scribed marked dedifferentiation of internal cell parts during regeneration in *Bursaria*. The ciliated adoral zone (az, Fig.
1-7), mouth, gullet, cortical plates of cilia (membranelles) and cytoplasmic vacuoles decrease in size or disappear in fragments isolated by

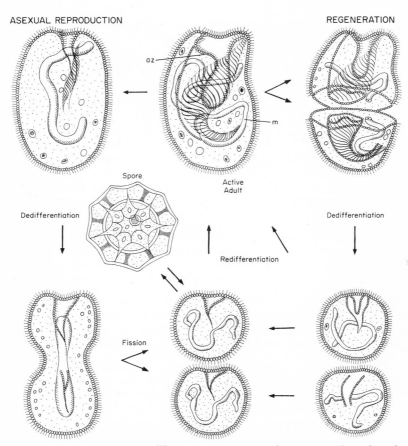

Fig. 1-7. Regeneration in a ciliate protozoan, *Bursaria*. Regeneration after the
animal is cut in two (on the right) can be compared with asexual reproduction
by transverse fission (on the left). Cytoplasmic dedifferentiation occurs during
both processes in *Bursaria*. The ciliated adoral zone is labeled (az), and the
macronucleus (m). (After E. J. Lund.)

injury, just as they do in animals preparing to reproduce by fission. For regeneration to occur, part of the macronucleus has to be included in each fragment, but its size is unimportant. Redifferentiation during regeneration is essentially identical in the two cases (Fig. 1-7, center). The dedifferentiation or simplification in structure of the macronucleus that occurs in both cases (see upper left, Fig. 1-7) is presumably related to the replication of nucleic acids and proteins which must ensue. Interestingly, cells that become spores or cysts in adverse conditions must dedifferentiate before redifferentiating into an active adult.

Stentor exhibits physiological as well as reparative regeneration. The mouth parts, for example, may be replaced from time to time (Balamuth, 1940; Tartar, 1961). During reparative regeneration in *Stentor,* oral structures always regenerate from the cut surface of the posterior piece and foot parts regenerate from the cut surface of the anterior piece. There is clearly a head to foot polarity and the factors responsible may reside in the cortex, along the so-called left boundary stripe (lbs, Fig. 1-3).

After surgical excision of the anterior end, regeneration requires about 12 hours in *Stentor*. It is essential that part of the macronucleus be present. During the first 4 hours the kinetosomes (centrioles associated with cilia) divide repeatedly. Then membranelle synthesis ensues and structural redifferentiation becomes apparent (Weisz, 1955). Bacteriostatic agents such as acriflavine prevent regeneration, presumably by affecting the kinetosomes. The effect is counteracted by nucleic acids and related compounds. Ribonuclease also prevents regeneration; this effect is alleviated by ribonucleic acid (RNA). Since the production of new cilia is dependent on protein synthesis, the system might be exploited for an analysis of genetic control of morphogenesis. Preliminary studies of cilia regeneration in Tetrahymena indicate that deoxyribonucleic acid (DNA) dependent RNA synthesis is required in some cases (Child, 1965). Such cells would also be excellent for an electron microscopic study of the morphogenesis of cilia and centrioles (see Williams, 1964). Cytological and physiological studies of regeneration in the other protozoans as well would be highly desirable. Most of the published work has been carried out on ciliates and flagellates (see reviews by Balmuth, 1940; Weisz, 1954; Tartar, 1961; and Berrill, 1961).

REGENERATION IN PORIFERA

Sponges display varying ability to regenerate after cutting. Those with a well-developed protective cortex are said to regenerate this part poorly (see Needham, 1952). The remarkable ability of sponges to reaggregate after dissociation of the component cells has been referred to above in the discussion of gemmule formation. In the in vivo situation, archaeocytes emerge from the gemmule, aggregate around it, and differentiate into a new sponge. In the in vitro experiments, the sponge is cut into bits that are strained through fine bolting silk (H. V. Wilson, 1907). The cells that emerge through the pores of the cloth reaggregate to form a new sponge (Figs. 1-8 and 1-9). Reaggregation is highly species specific. Recently, Hum-

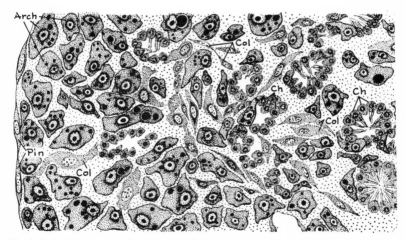

Fig. 1-8. Coalescence of dissociated cells from the sponge, *Ephydatia fluviatilis* 17 hours after filtration through bolting silk. Cells derived from the epidermis form a peripheral epithelium (Pin) which encloses the archaeocytes (Arch), collencytes (Col), and other mesenchymal cells, and the inner flagellated epithelial cells (Ch). Amoeboid movement brings the cells together, but the actual aggregation is due mainly to cell surface materials which are highly species specific. The large, basophilic archaeocytes give rise to an entire organism during asexual reproduction from gemmules, but other cell types are involved in morphogenesis after reaggregation. (After P. Brien, from *Growth, Development, and Pattern,* by N. J. Berrill. Copyright by W. H. Freeman and Company, 1961.)

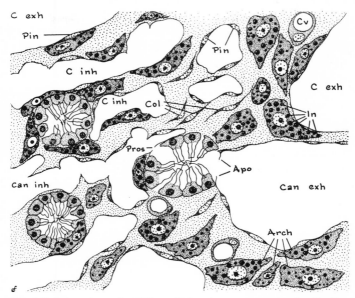

Fig. 1-9. Later stage of redifferentiation in an aggregate of cells dissociated from the sponge, *Ephydatia fluviatilis*. Exhalant and inhalant canals (Can exh, Can inh) lined with epithelium (Pin) have appeared. The canals are connected by inner chambers lined with flagellated epithelial cells (Ch). Archaeocytes (Arch), collencytes (Col), and other mesenchymal cells are taking up their definitive locations. By the fourth day following the dissociation of the sponge by filtration, the reaggregated cells have reformed a differentiated organism. (From *Growth, Development, and Pattern,* by N. J. Berrill. Copyright by W. H. Freeman and Company, 1961.)

phreys (1963) studied cells of *Microciona* dissociated in calcium-and magnesium-free sea water and concluded that the cells require the two divalent cations (calcium, magnesium) and a cell surface factor, possibly a normal intercellular material which is the species-specific factor, in order to reaggregate at a temperature cold enough to prevent the synthesis of intercellular matrix.

Wilson (1907) concluded that the archaeocytes or basophilic mesenchymal cells of the sponge have the greatest regenerative powers of any of the cell types, even though some of the others might undergo "regressive differentiation into an unspecialized amoeboid condition" under the conditions of isolation (see Huxley, 1911). The archaeocytes also are said to give rise to new tissues in growing sponges, in sponges reforming from gemmules, and in sponges regenerating after cutting. "Totipotent" reserve cells of this sort have been implicated in regeneration in coelenterates, flatworms, annelids, and certain tunicates, as we shall see now.

REGENERATION IN COELENTERATES

Various members of the three classes of coelenterates have been studied and found to be capable of restoring complete organisms from small fragments of the parents. Hydrozoa and Anthozoa, which occur as medusae and/or polyps, regenerate better than the Scyphozoa (jellyfish). Regeneration often parallels the process of budding described earlier in Hydrozoa (Figs. 1-4 and 1-5). Some authors have considered that the interstitial cells are reserve cells for all regenerative and budding processes in coelenterates. The evidence for participation of the interstitial cells in *Hydra* regeneration stems mainly from histological studies of normal regeneration. If a polyp is transected, the edges of the wound are brought together by contraction of the inner epithelium (the endodermis). The cells adhere to form a wound plug which is covered within an hour by epidermis. Interstitial cells adjacent to the wound seem to increase in size, divide, and migrate from epidermis into the endodermis, transforming along the way into endodermal cell types (gland or lining cells). Cell counts suggest that in both *Hydra* and *Tubularia,* the number of interstitial cells decreases in the rest of the body as the cells seemingly migrate to the wound area (see Tardent, 1963). In *Tubularia,* there is usually a rhythmical distal movement of cells along the stalk toward the regenerating area (Steinberg, 1955). These consist of (1) interstitial cells migrating between epidermal cells and (2) endodermal cells moving as a group (Tardent, 1963).

Further evidence for participation of interstitial cells in regeneration has been sought in experiments on irradiated animals. Interstitial cells seem particularly sensitive to x-ray and will degenerate if the dose of roentgen rays is high enough. The deleterious effect of x-ray on regeneration in coelenterates often is taken as evidence that interstitial cells are indispensable for regeneration (see Burnett, 1962; Tardent, 1963). There are, however, contradictory reports that *Hydra* can regenerate after irradiation, even though the interstitial cells are injured. Moreover, the possible effect of irradiation on other cell types usually is not taken into account in the interpretations of the inhibition of regeneration by effective doses of x-ray. X-ray could be expected to inhibit mitosis, not only of interstitial cells, but also of other cell types as well. Furthermore, the number of mitotic figures is said to remain low until redifferentiation has occurred in *Tubularia*. If this conclusion is valid, it is difficult to understand why x-ray would have any effect at all on the early stages of regeneration (Tardent, 1963). On the other hand, Burnett (1962) reports evidence of cell proliferation within 2 hours of wounding in *Hydra*. The problem of mitosis and radiation sensitivity obviously needs to be reinvestigated with newer techniques for studying cell turnover before the data can be applied in a meaningful way to an understanding of the origin of regeneration cells in Hydrozoa.

Haynes and Burnett (1963) have recently reopened the issue of the necessity of interstitial cells for regeneration in *Hydra,* using a different experimental approach. Taking advantage of the known fact that endodermis can give rise to epidermis in this animal, they selected a species, *Hydra viridis,* which lacks interstitial cells in the endodermis. The endodermis alone contains the algal symbionts that impart the green color to the animal and therefore this tissue is provided with an excellent marker for cell tracing experiments. The endodermis was isolated from the epidermis after treatment with trypsin by teasing the colorless outer epithelium away from the green inner epithelium. Even small fragments of pure endodermis regenerated partial or whole polyps. The mucous cells, zymogenic cells, and digestive cells of the endodermis became basophilic and seemingly dedifferentiated in part during the process. The endodermal cells transforming into epidermis lost the green algal symbionts in the process. Of considerable interest is the fact that new interstitial cells appeared in the regenerated epidermis and that these endodermis-derived cells gave rise to cnidoblasts just as would normal interstitial cells. Zwilling (1963) showed that isolated ectodermal fragments of another hydrozoan, *Cordylophora,* could reconstitute a whole animal. The ectoderm, however, contains interstitial cells as well as epidermal cells in this animal and it could be argued that only the former participated in the cell transformations that occurred. Steinberg (1963) studied a scyphozoan, *Aurelia*, which lacked interstitial cells in the ectodermal areas selected for study. She obtained good regeneration from isolated ectodermal fragments which contained no interstitial cells. It will be recalled that in the hydrozoan, *Limnocnida*, normal budding occurs in areas of the medusa which lack interstitial cells (Fig. 1-4). Regeneration also can occur in *Hydra* from regions of the body in which interstitial cells are injured or absent (Burnett, 1962; Diehl and Burnett, 1963). While a role in regeneration and budding cannot be denied to the interstitial cell, its major function in the adult is production of cnidoblasts. The evidence on hand as to the participation of more differentiated cells in regeneration is so strong, that it does not seem necessary any more to invoke the interstitial cell as a "reserve" embryonic cell to account for regeneration. Recognition of this fact calls attention to the need for a more detailed investigation of epithelial cytology during hydrozoan regeneration, with the possibility that cell dedifferentiation and proliferation in the formed tissues can be detected in all cases of regeneration in hydrozoans.

The phenomenon of polarity in regenerating systems has been extensively investigated in hydrozoans, especially in *Tubularia* (Fig. 1-10), where the process of regeneration can be followed very clearly in living animals observed through a dissecting microscope. *Tubularia* occurs in colonial clusters. The stalk (stem) of each animal contains a head (hydranth) with a distal whorl of short tentacles and a second proximal ring of long tentacles just below the gonophores. If the head is amputated, a broad zone of diffuse pigment appears in the endodermis adjacent to the tip of the stem after the wound has healed (Fig. 1-10, stage 3). The pigmented area is the primordium of the new hydranth (Fig. 1-10, stage 4). More discrete proximal and distal pigmented bands delineating the future location of the tentacles are next seen (Fig. 1-10, stage 5). Definite proximal ridges that will give origin to tentacles soon form (Fig. 1-10, stage 6). By the time the distal ridges appear, the proximal tentacles have started to separate from the stem (Fig. 1-10, stage 7).

Experiments combining proximal and distal parts of regenerating primordia in *Tubularia* are facilitated by the presence of an acellular perisarc around the stem, the speed of hydranth regenera-

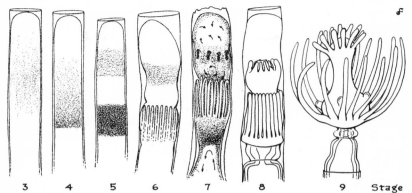

3   4   5   6   7   8   9   Stage

Fig. 1-10. Regeneration of hydranth from a cut *Tubularia* stem. Stages 1 and 2 are wound-healing stages. Stage 3 is characterized by the appearance of a diffuse pigmentation in the endodermis. The proximal limit of the pigmentation becomes clear at stage 4. This pigmented zone is subdivided into a proximal and distal band by stage 5. Ridges demarcating the proximal tentacles appear in the proximal pigmented band at stage 6. The proximal tentacles actually differentiate at stage 7 and now ridges demarcating the distal tentacles appear. At stage 8, the distal tentacles differentiate and a constriction develops which clearly delineates the proximal boundary of the new hydranth. Finally, at stage 9, the completed hydranth emerges from the stem perisarc. (From *Growth, Development, and Pattern*, by N. J. Berrill. Copyright by W. H. Freeman and Company, 1961.)

tion, and the availability of both red and yellow animals. Any region of the stem has the capacity to form any part of the hydranth, but it never reproduces that part which has already started to differentiate anterior to it (see Rose, 1957). If two like parts are joined at appropriate stages in regeneration, so that both face in the same direction, the one which is most anterior dominates development and tends to inhibit the proximal part (Fig. 1-11, A). The inhibitory information travels only from the distal to the proximal end. If a graft of a distal part (D′, Fig. 1-11, C) is put on the proximal end of the host, the proximal host region forms a second set of long tentacles, which has the imposed polarity of the graft (Rose, 1957). Experiments by Child and others have demonstrated similar proximodistal "gradients" in other species (Child, 1941; Barth, 1940, 1955; Berrill, 1961).

Child explains polarity in terms of a single physicochemical gradient passing from high intensity at the anterior end to low intensity at the base of the animal. Double gradient hypotheses also have been proposed (Tardent, 1963). Rose (1957) takes the view that differentiation in *Tubularia* is controlled by inhibitor substances moving in a distoproximal direction and he proposes a general theory of the role of specific inhibition in development which ties together many observed phenomena of this type. Numerous attempts have been made to isolate and characterize such inhibitor substances in hydrozoans, but the results have been inconsistent (see Steinberg, 1954; Fulton, 1959; Rose, 1963; Tardent, 1963).

It is possible that the electrical differences in potential between the anterior and posterior ends are responsible for movement of "correlative" substances in animals. Indeed, applied electrical fields can reverse the polarity of regenerating hydroids (Child, 1942; Lund, 1947; Barth, 1955). Rose (1963) found that an imposed current blocked control by a distal graft when the distal end faced the cathode. He placed agar-suspended homogenates of distal primordia of regenerating *Tubularia* inside cut stems and subjected the stems to an electric current. Those with their distal ends facing the cathode did not regenerate, but those facing the anode did regenerate. Rose suggests that positively charged particles (at pH 8.1, the pH of sea water) produced by the tissues and still present in the homogenate move toward the cathode to repress regeneration.

REGENERATION IN FLATWORMS

Polarity is a striking feature of regeneration in flatworms. The planarian may be cut up into pieces in any plane and each fragment normally regenerates a head from the anterior end and a tail from the posterior end (Fig. 1-12). If the piece is too small, a phenomenon called polar heteromorphosis occurs, with, for example, a posterior surface regenerating a head (Fig. 1-13, A). T. H. Morgan puzzled over this phenomenon and asked whether or not the greater chemical or physical difference between the two ends of a longer piece gave it a stronger polarity. Animals with more than one head can be produced by partially bisecting the worm and amputating the original head (Fig. 1-13, B). This phenomenon

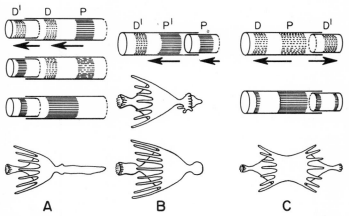

Fig. 1-11. Effects of distal parts on polarity of the regenerate in *Tubularia*. The dominance of distal over proximal parts can be studied by means of transplants between regenerates at stage 4, 5, or 6. (*A*) A presumptive distal tentacle region (D′) transplanted to the distal end of a whole primordium dominates the host, causing its distal primordium to reorganize as a proximal tentacle region. (*B*) A whole primordium (D′P′) transplanted to the distal end of a proximal part (P) at stage 6 eventually dominates and P reorganizes as part of the stem. Much the same effect is observed in a D′P′-D graft, except that the abortive tentacles formed by D persist. (*C*) If, however, the polarity of the two grafted parts is reversed (DP-D′) so that the distal ends of the two regenerates face each other, doubling occurs at P. Two new hydranths differentiate which face in opposite directions. The dominance of distal over proximal parts is interpreted in terms of an inhibitory effect on proximal parts exerted by the distal regions. (After S. M. Rose.)

is also classified as heteromorphosis (regeneration of a structure different from the normal). In this case, the normal polarity is preserved, but each half of the head "field" reproduces an entire anterior animal.

In transected worms, C. M. Child noted that heads regenerated at progressively posterior levels of the body are correspondingly smaller. He believed this to be due to a distoproximal gradient of metabolic quantities, especially oxygen consumption. Brønstedt (1955) has formulated a "time-graded regeneration field" to explain the observed decrease in the capacity for head formation posteriorly. The time required for head formation is correlated with the

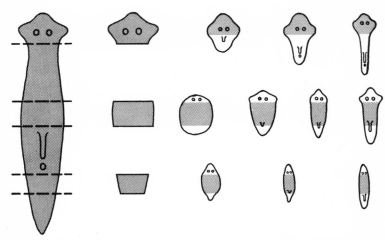

Fig. 1-12. Regeneration in the planarian flatworm. The distal portion of the fragment usually forms the new head and the proximal part the new tail. Considerable tissue reorganization must occur during regeneration for a complete, small worm develops from the cut fragment. The regenerate eventually grows to normal size. (After T. H. Morgan.)

"strength" of the head-forming field. If two pieces of the body are grafted together, one from a more anterior region, the anterior one forms head parts fastest and prevents the more posterior piece from forming a head. Brønstedt emphasizes the fact that the head-frequency curve not only decreases caudad but also from the middle line of the body toward both sides. The time required for regeneration of a head is longer the more laterally one goes and the more caudally one goes. Regardless of where the wound surface is located, there will always be a place (the most anterior and medial) where the head-building ability acts most energetically and in shortest time. This place will be the "high point" and determine the polarity of the regenerate (Brønstedt, 1955).

Wolff (1962) and Lender (1962) have reviewed the numerous experiments that have been done in their laboratories and elsewhere to uncover specific inhibitory and inducing substances that would explain the polarized organization of the planarian regenerate. Wolff proposes that interactions between the regenerate and the old tissue occur which reflect a succession of inductions and

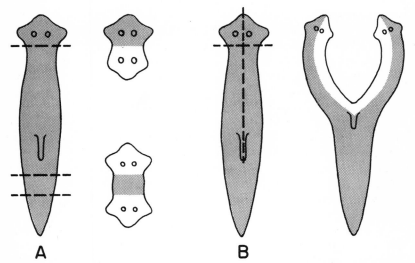

Fig. 1-13. (*A*) Polar heteromorphosis during regeneration in a planarian. The existence of this phenomenon has not received much attention in the explanations of polarity control which postulate inhibitory substances and graded electrical fields flowing from distal to proximal regions. The phenomenon tends to occur in very small fragments of worms. (*B*) Duplication of the head during regeneration of a bisected anterior half of a worm after amputation of the original head. Each lateral anterior half reorganizes into a whole. Information emitted from the distal parts and traveling proximally seems to act only on proximal parts, for two new heads develop as if each were unaware of the presence of the other. (After V. Hamburger.)

inhibitions, beginning when the anterior blastema forms. The first tissue to differentiate is the brain. The brain induces the eyes through the intermediary of diffusible substances. The prepharyngeal region then forms and induces the pharyngeal zone behind it. Inhibitory mechanisms are thought to intervene parallel with the inductive processes to prevent duplication of parts. Lender has partially isolated a diffusible substance from the brain that specifically inhibits development of brain tissue in a regenerate. Such diffusible inhibitory substances, operating on a cephalocaudal axis might account for Brønstedt's time-graded regeneration field. Since electrical fields can reverse polarity in flatworms, just as in coelenterates, it is tempting to conclude that the mechanism of diffusion of the postulated inhibitory substances is the same in planaria as in hydrozoans (Rose, 1963). Flickinger and Coward (1962) believe it is the favorable environment for protein synthesis in the head which normally accounts for head dominance. They studied the formation of secondary heads in worms treated with colcemide, a drug which obliterates the normally high anterior incorporation of CO_2 into protein.

As in the case of coelenterate regeneration, a continuing argument has existed as to whether or not "reserve" cells give rise to the blastema in planarian regeneration. In flatworms the cells in question are termed "neoblasts" and they reside in the mesoderm between the epidermis and muscle layers. The sequence of histological events after transection of a planarian is said to be as follows. The wound is covered within a day by epidermis. Undifferentiated-appearing cells then accumulate under the epidermis to form a blastema (Fig. 1-14) which proliferates and seems to form all of the new connective tissue, muscle, pharynx, and nervous system. The epidermis is said to derive normally from skin at the edge of the wound, and the intestine from proliferating endodermal cells in the cut end of the old intestine.

Wolff (1962) has argued that neoblasts are the primary cells of regeneration from the following evidence. After total body irradiation, planarians cannot regenerate. If the anterior half is irradiated and the head of such an individual amputated, a head will eventually regenerate. The delay is explained as a period in which healthy neoblasts from the tail migrate across the irradiated area to the cut surface. This interpretation, unfortunately, assumes that the epithelial tissues do not migrate across the irradiated area. Interestingly enough, a graft of unirradiated tissue will support regeneration in an irradiated planarian. It is argued that the neoblasts in the graft play the essential role. However, certain experiments on vertebrates suggest that unirradiated grafts do not necessarily supply regeneration cells, but may "revive" the irradiated tissues (Trampusch; Polezhayev; see Stinson, 1964).

The second line of evidence that neoblasts are the regeneration cells stems from cell counts. In these studies, neoblasts are identified by the oval or pearlike shape of the cells, the basophilic cytoplasm, and the well-developed nucleoli. In the normal animal, the number of mesodermal cells fitting this description diminishes from head

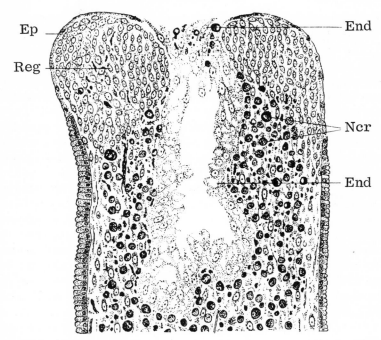

Fig. 1-14. Histological section of a regenerating flatworm. A thin wound epithelium (Ep) has migrated forward from the old epidermis to cover the cut end except for a central plug of regenerating endodermis that is continuous with the old endodermis (End). The origin of the regeneration cells (Reg) is debated, but the most popular theory is that they arise from reserve cells called neoblasts. The darker cells scattered throughout the tissue are necrotic (Ncr). (From J. Bandier, 1937, *Arch. Entwicklungsmech. Or.*, **135:** 326.)

to tail regions. Two days after decapitation, cell counts show that more basophilic cells are present near the sectioned surface than normal for that area. Seemingly they derived from the prepharyngeal region which subsequently replaces its neoblasts with new cells believed to have derived by proliferation of neoblasts in even more posterior regions (Lender, 1962; Wolff, 1962; Stephan-Dubois, 1965). The difficulty with this approach is that if a differentiated parenchymal cell transformed to a basophilic cell type by dedifferentiation as suggested by Woodruff and Burnett (1965), it would have been counted as a neoblast in this experiment (see also Chandebois,

1965). The problem clearly needs further investigation with more clear-cut cell tracing techniques.

The distribution of regenerative capacities among the turbellarians contradicts the popular assumption that all primitive animals regrow missing parts with ease. The capacity for anterior regeneration is restricted considerably in many of them. Members of the other flatworm classes, Trematoda (flukes) and Cestoda (tapeworms), are said to lack regenerative capacity, but they have not been studied thoroughly. Acoela, worms which belong to the same class as planarians (Turbellaria), lack organs such as kidney and gut and are said to have excellent regenerative capacities.

Passing on to the next phylum, Rhynchocoela (Fig. 1-1), we find that the nervous system begins to play an important role in regeneration. It has proved difficult to study the diffuse nervous system of coelenterates and experiments evaluating growth-promoting capacities of the nerve cords in flatworms are ambiguous. It seems clear, however, that nerve cord must be present for regeneration to occur in nemerteans (Fig. 1-15). Regeneration in Rhynchocoela (nemerteans) has been studied recently by Tucker (1959). The worms (*Lineus vegetus*) were cut into several pieces and the fragments were grown in brei obtained from homogenized heads, tails, or mid-pieces. Head brei inhibited anterior regeneration, whereas tail brei inhibited posterior regeneration, results reminiscent of those of earlier investigators on specific inhibition during regeneration in lower forms. The nemertean seems to lend itself readily to such experiments and perhaps will be the subject of further study along these lines. The protostome phyla intermediate between nemerteans and annelids have not been studied very extensively (Fig. 1-2). Among the mollusks, the cephalopods (squid, octopus) are said to regenerate arms and tentacles (Lange, 1920). The gastropods (snails) can reproduce a tentacle or an eye, but cannot replace an entire head. The pelecypods (clams) and gastropods repair parts of the shell, mantle, and foot (Korschelt, 1927; Needham, 1952; Hamburger, 1965).

REGENERATION IN ANNELIDS

The body plan of the annelid encompasses several major advances over that of the flatworm. There is, of course, a coelom.

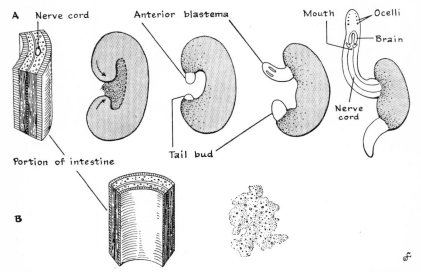

Fig. 1-15. Regeneration in the nemertean worm, *Lineus socialis.* The nervous system assumes a role of importance in regeneration in higher worms. In the nemertean, *Lineus,* regeneration occurs only in fragments which contain a section of one of the paired, ventral nerve cords (*A*). Fragments without nerve cord degenerate (*B*). The nerve may emit a trophic substance which stimulates the dormant parenchymal cells to transform into active regeneration cells. It may also direct the movement of the regeneration cells and the outgrowth of the blastema. (After W. R. Coe, from *Growth, Development, and Pattern,* by N. J. Berrill. Copyright by W. H. Freeman and Company, 1961.)

True segmentation has appeared for the first time in protostome evolution. A type of exoskeleton may be present, for example, the collagenous cuticle of the earthworm secreted by the single-layered epidermis. Each segment contains a kidney, usually with a nephrostome opening off the coelom. The brain contains a number of ganglia, innervation of muscles is rich, and advanced sense organs, such as eyes with separate lens and retina, often are present. Nerves are indispensable for regeneration in annelids. They penetrate the wound ectoderm and may produce neurosecretory hormones (Herlant-Meewis, 1964). A deviated nerve cord can bring about the development of supernumerary structures, but the specific structure induced depends on the particular body region that is so stimulated.

Considering the complexities in organization, it is surprising to find that some polychaetes and oligochaetes can reproduce asexually by transverse fission and that a number of them have the ability to regenerate whole worms from any fragment, even though the fragment lacks such important organs as gonads (see Berrill, 1961). The class Hirudinea (leeches), which is atypical in many other respects, does not share these remarkable regenerative capacities with Polychaeta and Oligochaeta (Fig. 1-2).

Polychaetes (marine worms) are so named because of the numerous lateral tufts of setae (chitinous spines used in locomotion). It is impossible to make a generalization about the regenerative capacities of the various genera. *Autolytus,* which has been studied by Okada (1929) and others, exhibits a clear-cut anteroposterior gradient in regeneration. As in planaria, the posterior regions tend to produce smaller heads, but a level is reached from which no head will form (Fig. 1-16, C). In some species only the first two segments can produce a head, whereas in others the last three can reproduce most of the body (see Berrill, 1961). Growth from the hindpiece forward is termed anterior regeneration. Growth from the amputated headpiece backward usually is more limited, but most worms regenerate well in this direction from any level posterior to the pharynx. In *Sabella,* a new head forms from the cut anterior end of the abdomen and later certain parts of the abdominal segments metamorphose into thoracic parts. If the abdominal piece is cut posteriorly at the same time so that it has two cut ends, then even more of the abdomen becomes thoracic in character. Rose (1957) explains these phenomena in terms of changes in the polarity of the animal, with corresponding differences in specific inhibitions of one region by another.

The class Oligochaeta includes the true earthworms, a number of primitive aquatic forms, and some intermediate groups that live in mud. In most oligochaetes, and some polychaetes, postlarval growth is by elongation of individual segments that were laid down earlier and are constant in number. Interestingly, posterior regeneration in these forms ceases when the total number of segments is restored to normal (Moment, 1951, 1953). *Lumbricus* is incapable of posterior regeneration and certain other earthworms

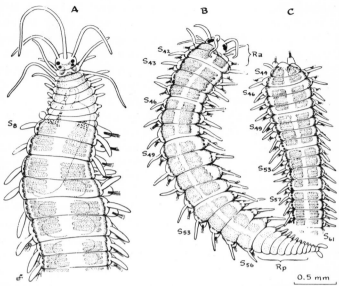

Fig. 1-16. Anterior regeneration in a marine annelid, *Autolytus pictus.* The size of the blastema affects the extent of redifferentiation and its size becomes smaller as one proceeds in an anteroposterior direction. A complete head and eight anterior segments regenerate from the sizable blastema that forms on the cut surface of segments 8 (*A*). Only a small, round cap bearing a semblance to a head (Ra) develops from the cut surface at segment 42 (*B*) and essentially nothing grows anteriorly from segment 44. Posterior regeneration (Rp) from segment 56 in *Autolytus* is depicted at *B*. Annelids vary in their capacity for anterior regeneration, but most can regenerate posteriorly from almost any level except the very anterior ones. (After Y. K. Okada, from *Growth, Development, and Pattern,* by N. J. Berrill. Copyright by W. H. Freeman and Company, 1961.)

can regenerate only during the diapause which occurs annually. Anterior regeneration is limited to anterior regions in most earthworms, but *Lumbriculus* can form a head from any level. In *Perionyx millardi,* polar heteromorphosis tends to occur in regeneration from an amputated headpiece. If the anterior head is removed later, the newly formed posterior head becomes dominant and tail regeneration ensues from the cut surface, thus reversing the original body polarity (Gates, 1951).

Posterior regeneration in the earthworm, *Eisenia*, has been studied extensively by Moment, who has formulated an electromotive theory to explain the controlling mechanisms. Moment found that the posterior tip of the worm is electropositive with respect to the rest of the body. The value becomes negative on amputation and gradually rises again during regeneration. In this worm, the total number of segments is 100. If the amputation level is at segment 80, then 20 new segments form; at segment 50, 50 new segments form. The acquisition of maximal electrical potential seems to be directly correlated with number of segments formed, not size of the segments. Moment (1953) postulates that animals continue to grow by proliferation of voltage-producing units, until, by summation of these units, a critical inhibitory voltage is built up. He calls attention to "Morgan's law of regeneration" which states that proliferative growth in all animals slows as the anatomical level of the amputation becomes more distal. Certainly, it seems clear that bio-electrical fields do exist from one end of the worm to the other (Smith, 1963) and that they may well exercise a control over regeneration in annelids as well as in nemerteans, coelenterates, and flatworms.

Judging from reports in the literature, the source of regeneration cells in annelids is variable. In *Euratella*, posterior regeneration after irradiation is said to be accomplished by epidermal cells which proliferate to form bands of mesoderm and other tissues (Stone, 1933). In other annelids, new intestine is produced by growth posteriorly from the old intestine (Berrill, 1961). The new nerve cord probably arises from the epidermis as in *Euratella*. In *Autolytus*, the new mesoderm is thought to arise from dedifferentiated muscle (Fig. 1-17). In *Nereis* and *Polydora*, it is said that the ectodermal, endodermal, and coelomic epithelia dedifferentiate (Herlant-Meewis, 1964; Thouveny, 1965). Dedifferentiated cells from all three germ layers and coelomocytes are also believed to form the blastema in *Nephtys*. The migratory cells from the coelom seem to attach to the surrounding ground substance when they reach the wound; then they lose their cytoplasmic granules and take on the appearance of dedifferentiated mesenchyme (Clark, 1965). In other annelids, neoblasts are thought to form the new mesoderm. In *Lumbriculus*, it is claimed that one or two neoblasts normally lie on the ventral side of the coelom in each segment and that they

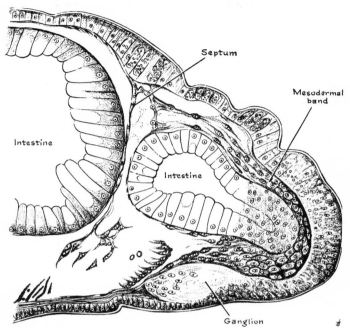

Fig. 1-17. Histological section of a posterior regenerate in *Autolytus*. Within 3 days, the epidermis has covered the wound and has started to grow inward along the ventral surface to give rise to nervous tissue (ganglion). The intestine and mesoderm reproduce themselves. They undergo a certain amount of dedifferentiation and redifferentiation in the process. At later stages, the intestine perforates through the epidermis to open to the outside. In some annelids, neoblasts in the mesoderm are said to give rise to regeneration cells during posterior regeneration, but not during anterior regeneration. The role of these so-called reserve cells in regeneration is debatable, however. (After Y. K. Okada, from *Growth, Development, and Pattern,* by N. J. Berrill. Copyright by W. H. Freeman and Company, 1961.)

migrate posteriorly when activated. In *Tubifex,* neoblasts are said to lie on the posterior face of the septa separating segments; in *Chaetopterus,* between the pair of nerve cords (see Berrill, 1961). While it is quite possible that there are real variations among annelids as to the ability of formed tissues to dedifferentiate and the presence or absence of neoblasts, it is tempting to believe that further study will reveal a common cellular mechanism underlying blastema formation in all the annelids.

REGENERATION IN ARTHROPODS

The jointed legs, chitinous exoskeleton, and specialized eggs of the arthropods, especially the insects, have proved eminently successful in allowing them to take to the land. There are 700,000 species of insects, most of them terrestrial (Fig. 1-2). The ability to regenerate the appendages is lacking or incomplete in all of these many kinds of adults (see Needham, 1965). The life of the adult insect is often so short that regenerative capacities seemingly would have little survival value. There is no asexual reproduction. The methods of producing eggs, however, are legion; in some insects parthenogenesis is the rule and there are no males.

During larval and pupal stages regenerative capacity is good in the insects. Bodenstein (1955) has induced the adult cockroach to regenerate a leg by causing it to molt. In one experiment a nymph is joined to an adult with an amputated limb. The adult molts as a result of hormone supplied to it from the nymph, and the leg regenerates (Fig. 1-18). The complex endocrine environment necessary for growth and reproduction in the insect has been studied fairly extensively in recent years (see Krishnakumaren and Schneiderman, 1964; Wigglesworth, 1964). In a recent review of the subject, Needham (1965) suggests that the initial phase of regeneration is controlled by juvenile hormone and does occur in the adult insect; the growth phase probably fails because of the lack of molting hormone (ecdysone). Nymphs can regenerate with an abnormal or incomplete nerve supply. It is possible, however, that minimal innervation of nonspecific nature is needed. The nerves do regenerate readily and may have been present in small numbers in the material studied (Bodenstein, 1955; 1957; Penzlin, 1964).

Wolsky (1957) has studied regeneration of antennae in nymphs of the milkweed bug. The regenerates always had one segment less than normal regardless of whether amputation was between the second and third, or the third and fourth, segments. The heteromorphic regenerates were often oversize. Wolsky explains this in terms of the unusual somatic polyploidy known to develop in some

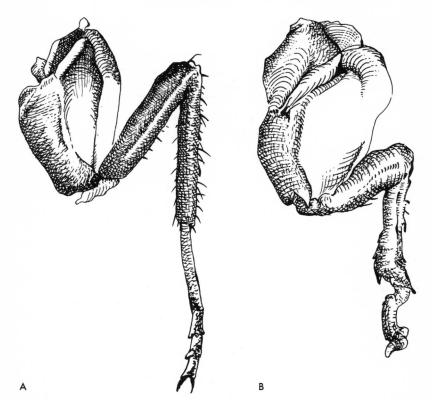

A   B

Fig. 1-18. Regeneration of the leg in a cockroach larva (*A*) and in an adult induced to molt (*B*). Insects regenerate appendages well during the long larval and pupal stage, but lose the capacity as adults. The adult can be induced to molt by supplying it with larval hormones. In the larva and molting adult, a leg will grow back after the first molt following amputation. Since the adult fails to cast off its exuviae, the regenerate has to be peeled out of its old skin and is light in color. (After Bodenstein, 1955, from photographs that orginally appeared in *J. Exp. Zool.* **129:** 209.)

insects by endomitosis. He speculates that the regenerating cells were larger as a result of polyploidy and so gave rise to a larger organ than the original. The polyploidy might have led to the abnormality of the regenerate. In any case, it is clear that a number of factors have to be taken into account in explaining growth and differentiation in the insect. These highly successful arthropods have developed nuclear and cellular specializations that are unheard of in other animals.

The class Crustacea is a little more straightforward than the Insecta. Lobsters, crayfish, and crabs continue to molt as adults and so presumably do not lose the necessary endocrine balance for growth and differentiation (see Bliss, 1959; Durand, 1960; Needham, 1965). In fact, they seem to have capitalized on this feature in evolving the phenomenon of *autotomy*. If the leg of a crab is seized, it breaks off spontaneously at a preformed point across the second leg joint by violent contraction of the extensor muscle of the leg. The wound is covered with a chitinous plug and a new limb does not grow out until the next molt. Chemical agents which irritate the muscle can bring about autotomy of the legs. Morgan (1901) has pointed out that even the abdominal appendages which are normally sheltered in the hermit crab can regenerate. The case is used in arguments against the adaptive significance of regeneration. A unique kind of heteromorphosis called homeosis occurs occasionally in arthropod regeneration. The classical example is the formation of an antenna instead of the normal eye stalk when the latter is amputated in the shrimp (see Morgan, 1901; Needham, 1965).

The origin of cells in regenerating crustacean limbs has been the subject of controversy (see Needham, 1952; 1965). Regeneration in continuity is impossible after autotomy. Morgan (1904) believed that the new muscles formed by dedifferentiation of ectoderm and he capitalized on this point to argue against the specificity of the germ layers (see also Schotté, 1940). The alternative to a local origin of cells from the epidermis is migration of cells with the ingrowing vessels and nerves. Since the developing muscle inserts on the exoskeleton, it must pierce the epidermis and this intimate contact may have given rise to the spurious impression that epidermis is transforming into muscle (Needham, 1952; 1965).

REGENERATION IN ECHINODERMS

Whereas the arthropods and annelids have evolved along the main line of protostomes, echinoderms represent an evolutionary branch of deuterostomes which seems to have led directly to the chordates (Fig. 1-2). Endoskeletons, absent in protostomes, are common in deuterostomes. The echinoderm has a calcareous skeleton which is formed by mesoderm in the deep layer of the skin. The water-vascular system is unique. The middle part of the left coelomic sac forms a ring around the esophagus and develops blind, radial canals from which the tube feet arise.

Starfish and brittle stars can regenerate arms from the central disc and can reform a whole animal from an arm, if part of the central disc is attached. Sea urchins can repair damage to the skeleton and tube feet. The sea cucumber responds to certain external stimuli by eviscerating the alimentary canal and other internal organs. The remaining shell of skin and muscle is capable of regenerating the autotomized organs. Certain sea cucumbers and starfish fragment at intervals to produce new individuals by asexual reproduction (Berrill, 1961; Hamburger, 1965).

The larvae of echinoderms do not seem to exhibit very great powers of regeneration nor do the larvae of annelids and tunicates. The larvae of *Arbacia,* which live about 4 weeks, do regenerate their arms. Adult echinoderms and annelids live longer than the larvae and, in general, have better capacities for regeneration. Needham (1952) suggests that regeneration probably is evoked too rarely in ephemeral (short-lived) forms to have survival value and therefore does not exist. This view seems overly teleological, however. Regenerative powers which have no survival value are not uncommon among animals, and it would not be surprising to find greater regenerative capacities among the echinoderm larvae, were they studied more thoroughly.

Anderson (1965) recently has extended his cytological studies of regeneration in echinoderm adults to include autoradiographic data on incorporation of tritiated thymidine. His article, and the book by Hyman (1955), serve as good introductions to the available literature on the origin of regeneration cells in this group. Anderson's earlier belief that mobilization of amoebocytes is responsible for regeneration of the caecum in sea stars was revised in the light of his autoradiographic studies which demonstrate considerable DNA synthesis in cells of the lining epithelium and covering peritoneum at all levels of the regenerate. For most of the other echinoderms, cytological data are not very clear cut. In holothuroids (sea cucumbers), it would appear that the anlage of the new gut derives from a solid cord of mesenchyme. Growth henceforth is by mitotic activity in the gut lining and the new layers are continuous with the old. In *Stichopus,* it is said that the lining of the gut proliferates and differentiates from mesenchymal aggregations without continuity of layers.

REGENERATION AND BUDDING IN TUNICATES

The Tunicata or Urochordata comprise one of three chordate subphyla. Their regenerative powers are truly remarkable, surpassing the subphyla Vertebrata and Cephalochordata, and the related phylum Hemichordata (Biberhofer, 1902; Needham, 1952; Berrill, 1961; Tweedell, 1961). The ascidians are found along most shore lines and have been studied in more detail than the oceanic classes of tunicates.

Ascidian eggs develop in typical chordate fashion, but they metamorphose into saclike animals that bear little resemblance to adult vertebrates and cephalochordates. As larvae, tunicates have a dorsal notochord, muscles, and a tubular spinal cord. At metamorphosis, the tadpole attaches to the sea bottom on its nose and the tail is resorbed by a remarkable process of cellular dissociation and migration. The epidermis then secretes an external tunic which contains collagen, cellulose, and a few cells. The barrel-shaped pharynx dominates the internal organs of the adult. Water enters through the branchial siphon and passes through gill slits in the vascularized pharyngeal wall into a peribranchial chamber that is connected to the exhalant siphon (Fig. 1-6). The digestive tract extends from the lower end of the pharynx to the base of the exhalant siphon. A glandular endostyle, neural mass, ovary and testis, heart, and circulatory system complete the structural complex.

Regeneration and asexual reproduction by budding are closely related processes in the ascidians. The epidermis, while highly differentiated and never itself seeming to transform into another tissue, may play an important role in the process. It is clearly the agent that isolates the fragments (Berrill, 1961). The inner tissues of the bud derive from different sources in different species: (1) the epithelium lining the atrial or peribranchial cavity, as in *Botryllus;* (2) the lining of the epicardium, a cavity adjacent to the heart; (3) the mesodermal septum separating afferent and efferent blood flow, for example, in the stolon of the colonial tunicates, *Clavelina* and *Perophora*. Participation of other organs has been described and attention has recently been called to a possible role of blood cells in budding in *Perophora* (Freeman, 1964).

Budding in *Botryllus* is part of a delicately timed reproductive process which involves simultaneous development of gametes and regular, precise dissolution of the parent zooid (Fig. 1-6). Maturation of the gonads coincides with full development of the bud, fertilization occurs, an embryo develops in the peribranchial cavity, and the parent zooid degenerates at a predetermined time. In the meantime, a second generation of buds has arisen in the zooid (Fig. 1-6). Premature dissolution (as by injury of the parent) simply speeds up maturation of the buds. If buds are extirpated, the survivors grow more quickly. Regeneration, then, might be said to be compensatory in nature in *Botryllus*.

Clavelina forms colonies of zooids connected by a stolon partitioned by a mesodermal septum into two vascular cavities. At the end of the breeding season, only the stolon is held over for the following spring and it will form the new buds that reproduce the colony. Pieces of stolon cut during this formative period regenerate from the cut ends, but later the cut ends merely heal over and new zooids are formed by compensatory regeneration at pre-established budding sites along the stolon piece. The septal tissue forms the inner vesicle that gives rise to the organs other than epidermis in the new bud. The body of the zooid is also capable of regeneration. If it is amputated below the thorax, a new thorax forms from epicardium and unites with the esophagus. Under certain conditions zooids of *Clavelina* during resorption form restitution bodies. All of the specialized cells regress, seemingly leaving the unspecialized epicardial tissue which is said later to proliferate and to reform new internal organs (see Berrill, 1961).

In another ascidian, *Perophora,* which also forms colonies on a vascular stolon, certain chemicals cause the zooids to regress and the organs seem to dedifferentiate to give rise to simplified, spheroidal cells which migrate back into the stolon (Huxley, 1921). The zooids also regress completely if they are injured by a cut. Later, new zooids form along the stolon. Is it possible that the new zooids arose from blood cells and dedifferentiated somatic cells or was growth entirely by septal proliferation as reported in normal budding? The stolon is quite transparent and the migration of cells from the cut zooid and their accumulation in the underlying stolon is easily visualized. In the summer of 1959 in Woods Hole, Massachusetts, I repeated Huxley's experiments on *Perophora viridis*. Pieces of stolon with one or more zooids were isolated in dishes and one zooid was amputated through the thorax or injured with a needle. The amputated zooid of the group described here (Fig. 1-19)

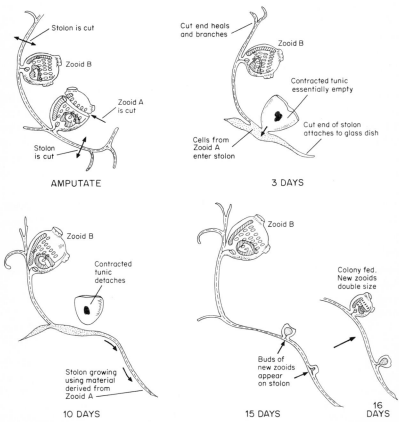

Fig. 1-19. Regeneration in a colonial tunicate, *Perophora viridis*. The individual animals, or zooids, of this urochordate are extremely sensitive to toxic agents. After amputation, the tissues of the injured zooid dissociate, the individual cells

contracted and maintained some circulation for a day. Three days later, the so-called dedifferentiation was complete and the underlying stolon, usually transparent, was full of green cells from the zooid. Soon, the cut end of the stolon nearest the accumulated cells began to grow. Within 2 weeks, a pair of new buds made their appearance on the stolon and all traces of the old mass of cells disappeared. Either the cells derived from the injured zooid or their nutritious by-products gave rise to the new growth, for the animals were not given a change of water and had no access to food. Stolons which did not seem to receive new cells from old zooids did not produce new zooids under the conditions of these experiments. Since the point of the work was to trace the fate of the old cells, zooids were labeled with tritiated thymidine and transplanted to unlabeled colonies. Some transplants took and regressed into the stolon after injury, but autoradiographs were unsatisfactory. Nevertheless, the feasibility of labeling ascidian tissues with isotopes and following the cells is attested to by the experiments of Sister Florence Marie Scott (1963) on *Amaroecium*. She was able to show by autoradiography that during the remarkable reconstitution of zooid that occurs in this species, the minced tissues inserted into a common tunic reaggregated like-tissues from like-tissues.

Certainly, there is very good reason to study these reproductive phenomena further in ascidians, as Barth (1955) has emphasized. *Clavelina* is easily obtained in Florida and the zooids are 2 cm long, as compared with 2 mm for *Perophora*. The ability for modulation exhibited by certain internal areas in ascidians, contrasted to the

---

apparently entering the stolon and later contributing to the formation of new buds. The drawings above show the course of events in a small portion of a *Perophora* colony transferred to a glass Petri dish and observed for 15 days without change of the water. The stolon distal to the injured zooid grows and gives rise to new buds, the migrating cells derived from the injured zooid A seemingly furnishing the substance. Whether these cells have actually dedifferentiated or merely serve as nutritive material for the growth of existing mesenchymal cells is not known. The colony was not fed up to the time of appearance of the buds and thus could not have used outside materials to build up the new buds. If such a colony is starved subsequently, the oldest zooids present on the stolon will dedifferentiate to furnish cells or nutritive materials to the buds. If, however, the colony is given a change of sea water on the fifteenth day, old zooids (as at B) persist and the new buds grow and differentiate by a process similar to asexual reproduction in this tunicate.

apparent rigidity of the epidermal cells, may have a bearing on the behavior of vertebrate cells. The important thing to realize, which seems to have been overlooked in choice of material for regeneration studies in the past, is that this group of invertebrates is more closely akin to the vertebrates than any other group which has been studied. It often is speculated that a primitive deuterostome related to an echinoderm larva gave rise to the chordates and, in one way or another, to the vertebrates. It is equally possible, as Berrill has suggested, that the larva was secondary; that some remote sessile tunicate, with a dorsal nerve net, produced the first larva with a dorsal spinal cord; that these cells, in these strange marine creatures, are more closely related to our own in behavior and genetic control mechanisms than to any cell in an insect, flatworm, or coelenterate.

> >
> >
> >
> >
> >

chapter two

Regeneration in Amphibians and Lower Vertebrates

EVOLUTIONARY ASPECTS OF VERTEBRATE REGENERATION

Regardless of the likely possibility that the vertebrates derived from the same primitive stock as did the echinoderms and uro-chordates, it is quite clear that they are a very different kind of creature in the present state of evolution. Asexual reproduction has been completely abandoned by the animals comprising the subphylum Vertebrata and a terrestrial habitat has been assumed by many. It is not known whether or not the primitive vertebrates possessed great regenerative powers. The immediate progeny of the ancestral vertebrates are, of course, animals which have under-gone further evolution (Fig. 2-1). The larvae of Petromyzontes, the so-called ammocoetes, are said to regenerate the tail (Niazi, 1964) and members of the superclass Pisces can regenerate the bony fins, optic nerve, and taste barbels (Nicholas, 1955; Goss, 1956; Haas, 1962). The fins cannot be cut too close to the body or they fail to regenerate. The anal fin of the male *Platypoecilus* loses the ca-pacity to regenerate in the adult, an irreversible loss which can be induced in the female as well by early treatment with androgens (Grobstein, 1947). Reports on the ability of adult fish to regrow a tail vary, but are generally negative. It seems clear that fish have little ability to replace the jaw. We do not know whether or not the Dipnoi and Crossopterygii, so closely related to the primitive amphibian ancestor, had any greater regenerative capacities than most modern fish.

The salamanders seem unquestionably to have the most re-markable regenerative abilities of all the vertebrates. With the possible exception of a few species (such as *Xenopus laevis*), regen-

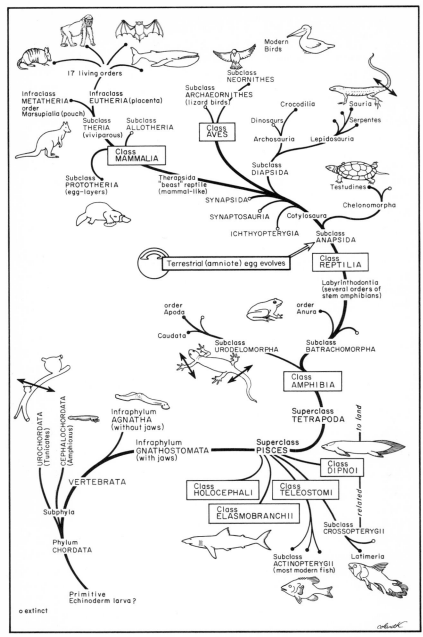

Fig. 2-1. Phylogeny of vertebrates. Animals that regenerate well are bisected by a double-ended arrow.

eration capacities seem quite limited in the adult anurans, yet these amphibians are more closely aligned with the main stem of evolution that gave rise to reptiles than are the urodeles (Fig. 2-1). It would be just as fair to say that the side-branch urodeles evolved new regenerative abilities as to make any claim that they retained something the higher vertebrates lost. In fact, the distribution of regenerative capacities among the urodeles supports such a speculation. Mechanisms for regenerating the lens are quite different among the salamanders. One family has the capacity to regrow the whole eye and optic nerve from the pigmented epithelium of the retina. Some adult land salamanders are said to regenerate the appendages well (*Plethodon*), others regenerate poorly (*Ambystoma*), and there is variability in regenerative capacity among the aquatic forms. Interestingly enough, a genetic mutation in the axolotl, which prevents this neotenic aquatic salamander from regrowing a limb, has been observed (Humphrey, 1966). It is tempting to think that a decrease in relative numbers of nerves accompanied by an increased threshold to the trophic action of the nerve is one cause for failure of limb regeneration among the higher vertebrates (Singer, 1952; Zika and Singer, 1965). Other possibilities will be considered at the end of the chapter, but it should be remembered that these comparisons are between the modern salamander and the modern frog or higher vertebrate. Nothing is known of the regenerative capacities of our prehistoric ancestors.

The frog larva is capable of regenerating the tail and hind limbs. The capacity to regenerate the hind limb is lost at metamorphosis, with the proximal parts losing the ability before the distal ones (Schotté and Harland, 1943; Van Stone, 1964). This response can be brought about by the hormone of metamorphosis, thyroxine, but thyroxine is not the "cause." The cause is the structure and function of the adult limb, its innervation, the controlling mechanisms for growth in these animals, and, ultimately, the genetics of metamorphosis. The effect is permanent, even if the thyroid is later removed from the animal. Embryos and young animals often are said to possess greater regenerative capacities than adults. There are so many exceptions to this statement, however, that it can hardly be called a rule. The transition which occurs from larva to adult during metamorphosis in the frog is best treated as a special phenomenon within that biological order.

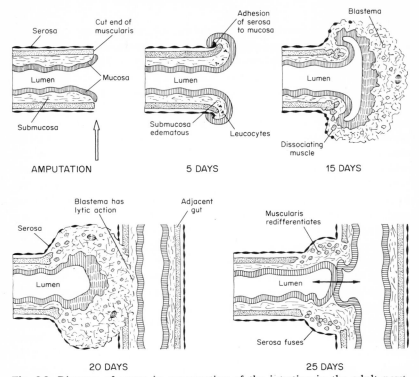

Fig. 2-2. Diagram of stages in regeneration of the intestine in the adult newt, *Triturus viridescens*. The animals were starved for a week prior to surgical transection of the intestine midway between the pylorus and rectum. Blood clots formed over the cut surfaces. The mucosa, which consists of columnar epithelium and a few associated connective tissue cells, tends to roll outward to fuse with the serosa (5 days). The connective tissue of the submucosa becomes edematous and contains many leucocytes during the initial inflammatory stage. By 5 days, the serosal and mucosal epithelial cells have begun to proliferate and definite dissociative changes are observed in the muscularis. The blastema which forms subsequently (15 days) contains proliferating cells derived from the dissociated smooth muscle and connective tissue of the gut wall. The growing epithelial cells of the serosa and mucosa are rounded and basophilic and may be difficult to distinguish at this stage from the mesenchymal cells of the blastema. The blastema has a tendency to adhere to any abdominal organ, and in so doing, it induces lysis of tissue and proliferation of cells in the area contacted. When the blastema adheres to another region of intestine, either end on or, as depicted above, laterally, the serosa and muscularis in the wall of the contacted intestine dissociate. The mucosa of the contacted intestine grows out toward the penetrating mucosa of the regenerate and fuses with it. The serosa, submucosa, and muscularis redifferentiate in continuity with the old wall. (After W. K. O'Steen.)

The reptiles derived directly from stem amphibians along the main line of evolution (Fig. 2-1), the most important advance being the acquisition of the terrestrial (amniote) egg. They have limited regenerative powers as compared with the urodele and frog tadpole, but nevertheless have evolved some interesting mechanisms which involve regrowth of body parts. The lizard discards its tail by a process of autotomy not unlike that which has evolved independently among the crustaceans (Chapter One). The regenerated tail, however, is far from perfect. Nerve and muscle are atypical and the cartilaginous axial skeleton does not segment or ossify (Woodland, 1920; Barber, 1944; Kamrin and Singer, 1955; Simpson, 1965). The embryonic lizard does not have the ability to regenerate the tail (Moffat and Bellairs, 1964).

Reports of regeneration among the birds and mammals emphasize the variability of the process. Physiological regeneration is quite well developed. Epidermal appendages, such as feathers, nails, and hairs, either grow continuously or are replaced by periodic molts, as was also probably true of the scaly epidermis of our immediate terrestrial ancestors. Regeneration of functional axons in the central nervous system is better developed in birds than in mammals and perhaps is better in embryos than adults (Windle, 1955). Mammals have a remarkable ability for liver regeneration (Chapter Three). In fact, this particular capacity seems better developed in higher vertebrates than in salamanders.

The salamander, because of its dramatic regenerative responses, has been the subject of much study in the past and will receive most of our attention in this chapter. In particular, we shall consider the regeneration of the lens, retina, and optic nerve, and the regrowth of the limb. This does not mean that other parts of the body have not been studied. Nor are they less interesting. Regeneration of the urodele tail, bony vertebra, and spinal cord, but not of the notochord, occurs readily (Piatt, 1955; Holtzer, 1959). There is no direct evidence that differentiated nerve cells can divide. In the regenerating spinal cord of the urodele larva, cells are "paid off" from the transected gray matter to cross the ablation gap; the neuroblasts that give rise to new motor neurons may have derived from ependyma (Butler and Ward, 1965). Goss and Stagg (1958) report that the newt jaw regenerates after complete amputation or excision of the central portion, if enough mandible is left to sup-

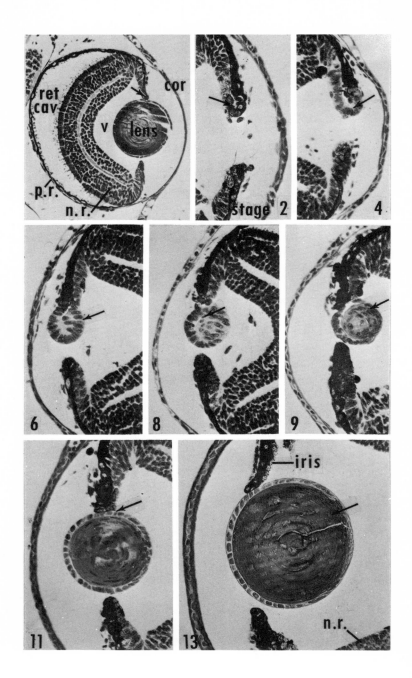

port the process. Regeneration of the intestine is excellent in both frogs and newts (see O'Steen, 1958; 1959). The loose ends find each other and rejoin end to end or side to side (Fig. 2-2). The blastema forms by dedifferentiation, but during redifferentiation the cells are believed to sort out according to their origin (O'Steen and Walker, 1962).

Fig. 2-3 (*Facing page*). Lens regeneration in the adult newt, *Triturus viridescens*. Stages shown (2, 4, 6, 8, 9, 11, and 13) are labeled according to Reyer, after Sato. The upper left-hand photograph is a section of the unoperated eye for orientation. The lens and the cornea (cor) are of the same embryological origin (ectoderm). The iris (arrow) and retina arose from the optic cup. The two layers of neuroectoderm that comprise the iris are continuous with the pigmented layer of the retina (p. r.) and the neural retina (n. r.). The two layers originally lined the optic vesicle and a potential free space exists between them, the intraretinal cavity (ret cav), the size of which is often exaggerated by fixation artefact as in the photograph. Stimulatory factors from the neural retina (n. r.) diffusing through the vitreous (v) are believed to influence lens regeneration.

Four days after the lens is removed, a slight thickening of the dorsal iris becomes visible (stage 1). Then, a cleft appears between the two layers of the iris (arrow, stage 2). At 6 days, depigmentation of the iris margin begins (stage 3) and a hollow vesicle lined by cuboidal cells becomes apparent (arrow, stage 4). At 8–9 days, the cells of the posterior wall of the vesicle elongate (stage 5) and acidophilic lens fibrils first become detectable in these cells (arrow, stage 6). By stage 7 (11 days) the posterior cells have enlarged to form a definite "primary lens nucleus," which soon obliterates the lumen of the vesicle (arrow, stage 8). At 16 days, secondary lens fibers (arrow, stage 9) begin to develop from the equatorial zone of the vesicle. A medial lens suture appears (stage 10) and the secondary lens fibers enclose the primary lens nucleus completely. At about 18 days, the new lens detaches from the iris (arrow, stage 11). The lens continues to grow and eventually the nuclei of the lens fibers (arrow, stage 13) are obliterated by the newly forming lens proteins. The number of days required to reach each stage varies with temperature differences and other factors.

It is convenient to group the stages into four periods. Period I (latent period): stages 1 (4 days) and 2 (5 days). Slight thickening of iris. Period II (initial period): stages 3 (6 days), 4 (7 days), 5 (8 days), and 6 (9 days). Dedifferentiation, increasing DNA and RNA synthesis, cell proliferation. Period III (lens fiber formation): stages 7 (10 days), 8 (11 days), 9 (12 days), 10 (16 days), and 11 (18 days). Primary and secondary lens fibers form and protein synthesis increases. Period IV (growth): stages 12 (20 days) and 13 (30 days). Nuclei of primary lens fibers disappearing, nuclei of secondary fibers disappearing. × 135. (Courtesy of R. W. Reyer, from photographs that originally appeared in the *Quart. Rev. Biol.*, 1954, **29**: 3–4.)

REGENERATION OF THE LENS

The amphibians vary in their ability to regenerate a lens and in the types of cells which are used for the purpose. Certain anurans and salamanders of the family Ambystomidae are able to regrow a new lens from a fragment of the old lens. Members of the family Salamandridae have the remarkable ability of growing a new lens from the dorsal iris, a rather startling metaplasia considering that the iris is, embryologically, part of the brain whereas the lens is part of the surface ectoderm. Interestingly enough, the larval South African frog, *Xenopus laevis,* more closely reduplicates the embryonic process in regenerating a new lens. An invagination of surface ectoderm, which is the corneal epithelium in this case, gives rise to a ball of cells that transforms into the new lens (Freeman, 1962; Overton, 1965).

Regeneration of the lens from the dorsal iris (Wolffian regeneration) has been studied more extensively than any other type of lens regeneration (Stone, 1959; Reyer, 1954; 1962). When the lens is removed in *Triturus viridescens,* the pupillary margin of the dorsal iris swells (arrow, Fig. 2-3) and a cleft appears between the two epithelial layers in the area corresponding to the cavity of the original optic cup (stages 1–2, Reyer, 1954). Then, the cells of the dorsal iris begin to depigment, their nuclei enlarge and the regenerating mass takes the shape of a vesicle (stages 2–4, Fig. 2-3).

Fig. 2-4 *(Facing page).* Immunofluorescence of γ-crystallin proteins in the regenerating lens. Antiserum to purified gamma crystallin from adult newt lens was obtained by injecting the newt antigen into rabbits. Antiserum labeled with fluorescein isothiocyanate was applied to sections, which were then viewed in a fluorescent microscope with an ultraviolet light source. In each photograph, the light area is fluorescent. The corneal (anterior) side of the lens is uppermost and the retinal (posterior) side is lowermost. Slight fluorescence of a few cells in the posterior wall of the lens vesicle was detected at 13 days in these experiments (stage 5, shown at *a*). Reactive cells have ceased dividing. At stage 6, when acidophilic lens protein is detectable in the cytoplasm with the light microscope, fluorescence in the elongating inner cells is stronger (*b*). At stage 10, after the secondary lens fibers have started to form, there is intense fluorescence in all fiber cells, but none in anterior epithelial cells (*c*). Nonreactive cells divide in the equatorial zone at the junction of anterior epithelium and posterior wall, stop making DNA, and then transform into lens fibers. The cell nuclei eventually are obliterated almost completely by intranuclear lens proteins (*c*). (Courtesy of

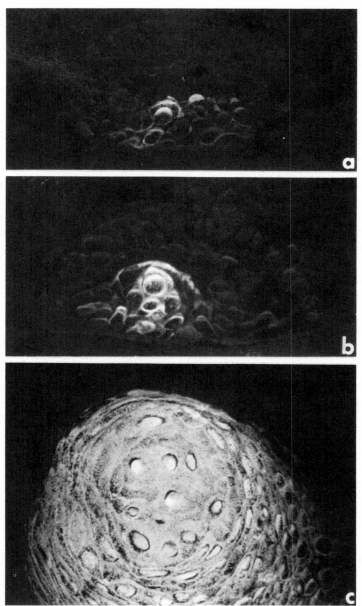

C. Takata, J. F. Albright, and T. Yamada, from photographs that originally appeared in *Science*, 1965, **147**, no. 3663, 1299.)

During the process of dedifferentiation the cells begin to divide, RNA synthesis reaches a peak (5–7 days), and cytoplasmic basophilia increases. New protein synthesis increases markedly by 8 days (Yamada and Takata, 1963). Electron microscopy has clarified the process by which the pigment granules are extruded from the cells and taken up by macrophages and also has demonstrated that the proliferating cells are relatively undifferentiated in appearance (see Karasaki, 1964). The growing cells increase in height between stages 5 and 8 and the posterior layer bulges into the lens cavity (stage 6, Fig. 2-3). The specific proteins that now form in the posterior cells are detectable (Fig. 2-4) by immunochemical procedures (see Takata *et al.,* 1964, 1965). The new fibrillar lens proteins impart an acidophilic staining reaction to the cytoplasm. The lens cavity soon is obliterated by the primary lens fibers (stage 8) and secondary fibers form around centrally located primary fibers (stages 9–11, Fig. 2-3). At this time there is a rapid increase in tritiated leucine uptake and the bulk of the lens proteins are laid down in the cell cytoplasm (Yamada and Takata, 1963). The new lens separates from the iris (stage 11) and by 30 days after removal of the original lens (stage 13), the regenerated lens is almost full size (Fig. 2-3). The nuclei of the lens fibers gradually lose their basophilic staining characteristics and seem to become filled with lens protein.

Numerous experiments have been done which indicate that the neural retina is the source of a stimulus (retinal factor) necessary for lens regeneration (see reviews by Stone, 1959; Reyer, 1962). For example, a pliofilm disc inserted into the eye so as to isolate the iris from the neural retina completely inhibits lens regeneration. The anterior-posterior polarity of the new lens also depends on the retina. A competent neural retina, as in *Triturus,* cannot, however, stimulate an incompetent iris, as in *Ambystoma,* to produce a new lens. Not all regions of the *Triturus* iris can produce a lens; the capacity falls markedly as one proceeds from the dorsal to the ventral pupillary margin. Moreover, dorsal, but not ventral, pigmented retinal epithelium can regenerate a lens in the absence of the original iris. The retinal epithelium does not become competent to do this, however, until fairly late in embryonic development (Reyer, 1962).

The immediate stimulus to lens regeneration is removal of the lens. No actual injury or "wound" is necessary. The idea prevails that a normal lens exerts an inhibitory effect which prevents another lens from forming. Experimental evidence for this concept is abundant (see reviews by Reyer, 1962; Goss, 1964). The old lens does not act as a mere mechanical obstacle, nor does it inhibit new lens formation simply by serving as a barrier through which the retinal factor described above cannot pass. It has been suggested that the old lens uses up retinal factor and thus impedes development of a new lens. There is also some evidence for the theory that the lens secretes a substance that neutralizes the growth-stimulating action of the neural retina. The most popular idea, however, is that the lens secretes an inhibitory substance which prevents more of itself from forming. The system may prove to be a good model for studying the role of specific inhibition in the control of development. Most vertebrates seem to be able to replace excised portions of the lens by localized compensatory growth (Goss, 1964).

REGENERATION OF THE RETINA AND OPTIC NERVE

In the majority of urodeles that have been studied, pigmented layer of the retina has been found to be capable of regenerating the neural retina and this, in turn, the optic nerve. Thus, it is possible to transplant eyes from one salamander to another and study the effect of the position of the eye on visuomotor responses (see reviews by Stone, 1959; Reyer, 1962). When an adult salamander eye is transplanted, the neural retina (Fig. 2-3, n.r.) degenerates. The pigment layer (Fig. 2-3, p.r.) then proliferates from a single layered to a multilayered epithelium. The cells lose pigment granules as they enlarge and divide. A new intraretinal cavity (Fig. 2-3, ret cav) forms in the thickened epithelium. The original "free" side of the pigment layer (the side originally facing the intraretinal cavity) becomes a basal surface apposing the vitreous body. Mitoses, as in normal retinal development, are along the newly created free surface that delineates the presumptive neural retina from the outer epithelium that will be the new pigment layer. Rods and cones differentiate along the free surface of the neural retina, presumably from projecting cilia, as in the embryo. The optic nerve grows back from the new ganglion cell layer on the vitreous or "basal" side of the neural epithelium.

Anuran tadpoles are able to grow new neural retinas from the pigment layer and iris, but adults are said to lack this ability, although they can regenerate optic nerve from the neural retina. Certain other vertebrates, such as the reptiles and fishes, may have limited abilities along these lines (see reviews in Windle, 1955). Coulombre and Coulombre (1965) have recently reported regeneration of the neural retina in the chick embryo from the margin of the optic cup or from pigmented epithelium a distance away from the margin. Some neural retina must be present, but it has to be separated from the pigment layer. The simplest stimulus to regeneration is a foreign object inserted between the two layers, in the intraretinal space of the optic cup. Interestingly enough, rods and cones of the new retina face neural retina regenerated from the optic cup edge (arrow, Fig. 2-5). New optic nerve is forced to grow out into ordinary connective tissue instead of along the vitreous body, an interesting case of regeneration of no "survival value" to the animal (see Needham, 1952, p. 131).

REGENERATION OF THE LIMB

No organ or organ system has been studied so extensively as the amphibian limb in attempts to understand the elusive factors that bring about regeneration. When the limb of a salamander or frog tadpole is amputated, the cells in the formed tissues of the

---

Fig. 2-5 (*Facing page*). Regeneration of the neural retina in the chick after removal of the original neural retina from 4-day-old embryos. A fragment (n. r.) of neural retina must be reimplanted in the vitreous to stimulate regeneration from the pigment layer of the retina (p. r.). Two days later, the pigment layer has proliferated (arrow, *A*), to form a small patch of relatively undifferentiated cells which is the anlage of the new neural retina (n. r.'). Three days after the operation, the regenerating patch in the pigmented retina is considerably thickened (n. r.', *B*). The epithelium still recognizes its former free surface, for all of the mitotic figures (arrow) are along the intraretinal border. Ten days after the operation, the new retina regenerated from the pigment epithelium has differentiated (n. r.', *C*). Another neural retina (n. r.) has grown from the edge of the optic cup. Its ganglion cells are innermost and its rods and cones face outward, as is the case in normal development. In the regenerate (n. r.') from the pigment layer, however, the rods and cones are on the inside (arrow) and the ganglion cells on the outside, an arrangement that would be useless physiologically. *A* and *B*, × 550. *C*, × 240. (Courtesy of J. L. Coulombre and A. J.

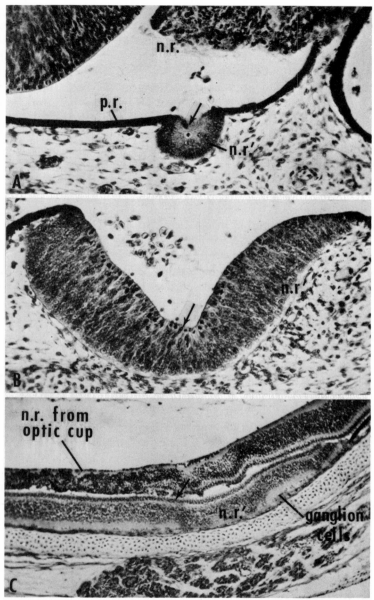

Coulombre, from photographs that originally appeared in *Devel. Biol.* 1965, **12:** 84, Copyright © 1965 by Academic Press, Inc.)

remaining stump dedifferentiate to produce a large bud or *blastema* that subsequently grows rapidly and then redifferentiates into a complete limb. These events are initiated by the injury to the stump (Rose, 1944; Thornton and Kraemer, 1951) and they are controlled by nervous and hormonal factors (Schotté and Butler, 1944; Singer, 1952–1960; Schotté, 1961). Limb regeneration, however, is essentially a local process. A starved animal regrows its limbs as fast as a well-fed animal. The presence of more than one regenerating part on an animal does not affect the rate of regeneration. The origin of the cells is from within the limb itself. The limb of a larval salamander will regenerate from the unirradiated distal tip of a stump even if the proximal part is x-rayed, but if the distal amputated portion is x-rayed the limb will not regenerate (see Butler, 1935; Butler and O'Brien, 1942; Brunst, 1950).

The factors which determine the pattern of differentiation of the limb regenerate are not well understood. It generally is believed that a period of determination ensues prior to visible differentiation, as the blastema begins to elongate, but it is difficult to obtain critical experimental evidence for this concept (see Weiss, 1939; Needham, 1952). The limb stump and the adjacent shoulder region seem to act as a "limb field" to influence the differentiation of the regenerate (Weiss, 1939). A limb split in half prior to amputation will produce two regenerates, much as a bisected planarian produces two heads (Chapter One) and, here again, there seems to be some sort of a bioelectric field within the limb which accounts for, or contributes to, the polarity of the system (Becker, 1961). A striking example of the distoproximal control of the polarity of the limb stems from the work of Butler and others on reversed limb transplants (see Deck, 1955). Provided that sufficient reinnervation occurs, a limb transplanted onto another site with its distal end placed proximally will grow distal parts from the cut proximal surface.

Within the limb field, it is possible to produce supernumerary limbs by deviation of nerves (Bodemer, 1958) or by localized ultraviolet irradiation (Butler and Blum, 1963). The source of the nerve is unimportant because the character of the outgrowth is determined by the limb field, not the nerve. A considerable amount of work has been done to discover which of the old limb tissues determines the character of the new outgrowth. Glade (1963) has reinvestigated the role of the skin and reports that tail ski taillike bones to form in a limb regenerate. Weiss, Bischle ton, and others have studied limb regeneration after exarticulation of the skeleton. The regenerate differentiates a skeleton even though the stump lacks one. Tail muscle transplanted to x-rayed limbs gives rise to regenerates with taillike muscle and no skeleton, whereas limb muscle transplanted to x-rayed limbs gives rise to limbs with muscle and skeletal elements (Thornton, 1942). The effect of implants of normal and cancerous tissues has been studied by Ruben, Deck and others (Ruben and Balls, 1964; Stevens *et al.,* 1965). A number of other experiments have been done along these same lines in the past (see reviews by Weiss, 1939; Needham, 1962; Trampusch, 1959; Glade, 1963; Rose, 1964). It must be admitted, however, that the exact nature of the tissue, or tissue interaction, responsible for the differentiation of the limb pattern remains an enigma. In the ensuing sections, we shall devote considerable attention to studies on cell structure and function in regenerating limbs in order to illustrate the manner in which cytological techniques have been applied to the problem of regeneration. Then, we shall return to the intensely investigated subject of the role of epithelium, nerves, and hormones in limb regeneration.

ORIGIN AND GROWTH
OF THE REGENERATION BLASTEMA

Butler (1933) and Thornton (1938) described a histological sequence of events in the amputated forelimb of the *Ambystoma* larva whereby the formed tissues of the stump dedifferentiate to yield the growing mesenchymal cells of the blastema. The cells near the cut end of the cartilaginous humerus begin to enlarge and round up within 3–4 days after the amputation and the cartilaginous matrix then regresses, releasing the cells from their capsules. As cells begin to divide, they assume the general morphological characteristics of mesenchymal cells. It is possible to observe the sequence of events with the light microscope in fingers of living animals (Hay, 1962). The observations on living animals emphasize the fact that the blastema arises "backwards" at the expense of the old stump. Cartilaginous matrix regresses for a considerable distance proximally, releasing enlarged cells, which have already begun to

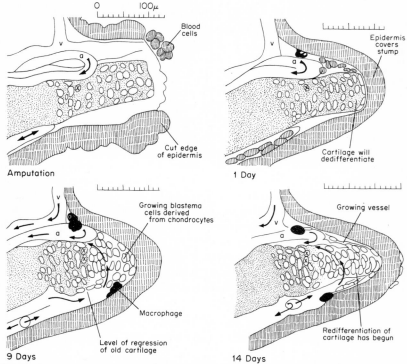

Fig. 2-6. Regeneration of the finger of a living *Ambystoma* larva. Following amputation (Amp) of the proximal phalanx, the anesthetized animal was placed in a small chamber and observed daily with a compound light microscope. The same artery (a) and vein (v) appear in each drawing and are used to orient the scale that appears in the upper right corner. It can be seen that for at least 9 days following amputation, there is no substantial increase in length of the cut finger. All of the cellular changes that give rise to the blastema occur proximally within the old stump. Epithelium migrates across the cut surface within a few hours after amputation. Two to three days later, the distal cartilage matrix begins to disappear, releasing the cells which concomitantly enlarge and assume the morphology of mesenchymal cells. Cell division begins during this period of dedifferentiation and therefore the early blastema contains more cells than were present in the old cartilage. Continuing cell proliferation leads to elongation of the regenerate and soon redifferentiation begins (14 days). The arrows indicate the direction of blood flow. In the drawing on the lower right, the endothelium which will give rise to new vessels is depicted growing forward along the sides of the blastema.

56

divide during the process of dedifferentiation (Fig. 2-6). The changes in the stump muscle of the limb are of the same type (Figs. 2-7–2-9). Electron microscopic studies confirm Thornton's observations that the formed myofibrils disappear and the syncytial fibers break up into individual cells during dedifferentiation (Hay, 1959). Dedifferentiation is more complete in the distal areas than in the most proximal regions, but the process extends for a considerable distance back into the stump. Schwann cells and connective tissue cells also contribute to the blastema (Butler, 1933; Thornton, 1938).

Some of the muscle cytoplasm is lysed and probably is phagocytosed by macrophages and leucocytes (see review by Trampusch and Harrebomée, in Kiortsis and Trampusch, 1965). Macrophages

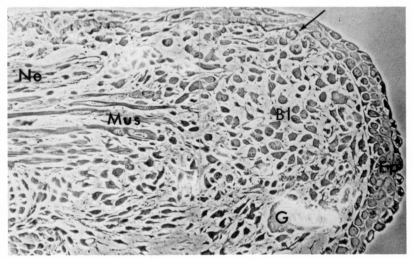

Fig. 2-7. Longitudinal section of a regenerating larval *Ambystoma* limb 5 days after amputation. The section passes lateral to the cut humerus, grazing a portion of the perichondrium, an associated osteoclast at G, and several dedifferentiating muscle fibers at Mus. The blastema cells which appear at Bl have probably arisen largely from muscle fibers that were originally present in this area. Schwann cells from the cut nerves (Ne) and connective tissue cells also contribute morphologically undifferentiated cells to the blastema. The apical wound epidermis (Ep) is at least five layers thick, whereas the epidermis over the rest of the young larval limb is two to three layers thick. The cut end of the fibrous basement lamella, the dermis of the larva, is indicated by the arrow. × 130. (From E. D. Hay, *Devel. Biol.*, 1: 558, Copyright © 1959 by Academic Press, Inc.)

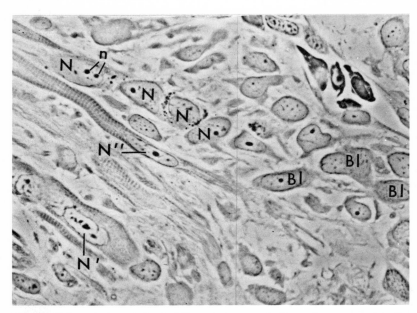

Fig. 2-8. Enlarged view of the dedifferentiating muscle fibers that appeared in the preceding figure (Mus, Fig. 2-7). During the process of dedifferentiation, the normally elongate nucleus of the muscle cell (N″) enlarges (N′), and becomes rounded in shape (N). These changes herald the beginning of DNA synthesis. The row of vesicular nuclei at N probably all derived from one dissociating fiber. The fate of the formed myofibrils and old cytoplasm is obscure. Nucleoli (n) are prominent, for the cells are synthesizing RNA as well as DNA. Blastema cells (Bl) derived from muscle and the other inner tissues have large vesicular nuclei and scanty cytoplasm which is basophilic when viewed in the light microscope after application of an appropriate stain. × 465. (From E. D. Hay, *Devel. Biol.*, 1: 558, Copyright © 1959 by Academic Press, Inc.)

can be readily identified in electron micrographs and it is interesting to note that these phagocytic cells do not contain fragments of myofibrils. The myofibrillar debris seems to break up into unidentifiable materials before it is removed. Multinucleated giant cells that are probably derived from monocytes or macrophages seem to assist in removal of osseous and cartilaginous debris (Hay and Fischman, 1961). Histochemical studies indicate an intense acid phosphatase reaction in the leucocytes, macrophages, and dedifferentiating tissues, reflecting a probable role of cytoplasmic lysosomes

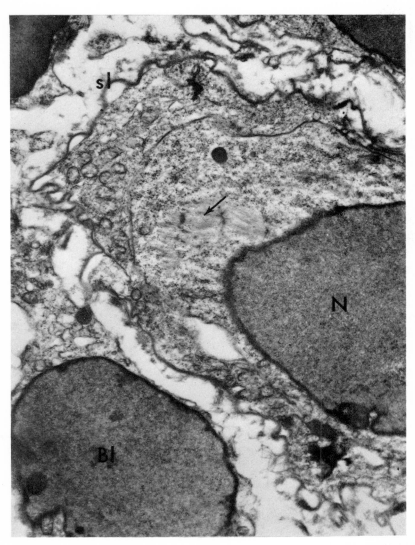

Fig. 2-9. Electron micrograph of a dedifferentiating muscle fiber. The myofibrils (arrow) break up and disappear completely. The basophilia of the cytoplasm of the blastema cells is due primarily to new ribonucleoprotein granules (ribosomes) which appear in the cytoplasm during dedifferentiation. The blastema cell (Bl) also contains granular endoplasmic reticulum, mitochondria, and a

in the reabsorptive processes (Schmidt and Weary, 1963). In the adult salamander, it would seem that lactic dehydrogenase activity in the tissues increases during the phase of blastema cell accumulation and proliferation, whereas during later proliferative stages, succinic dehydrogenase prevails. Thus, it is possible that metabolism tends to be glycolytic during the stages of dedifferentiation and early proliferation (Johnson and Singer, 1964).

As the dedifferentiating cells transform into blastema cells, the nuclei enlarge and become vesicular (lightly staining), the nucleoli become more prominent, and the cytoplasm takes on a basophilic staining reaction. These are the characteristics of growing cells actively engaged in DNA and RNA synthesis and protein synthesis and, indeed, it can be demonstrated that these are the important new metabolic activities of dedifferentiating tissues (see Anton, 1961; 1965; Hay, 1962; and Chapter Four). The blastema cells are similar in their morphology, regardless of whether they are derived from cartilage or muscle, or from Schwann cells and connective tissue cells (Fig. 2-10). In the larva, free ribonucleoprotein granules are prominent in the cytoplasm whereas in the adult, endoplasmic reticulum is well developed (see Chapter Four).

As a result of dedifferentiation and the concomitant proliferation of the inner cells, the old tissues of the stump are replaced by a bud of embryonic-appearing cells which grows out as a conical-shaped blastema (Fig. 2-11). The cone stage is the period of most active proliferation (Chalkley, 1959). Very soon, however, the regenerate begins to differentiate a new limb. The cartilage anlagen appear and the blastema assumes a more flattened contour (paddle stage). When the new skeleton is clearly demarcated, the regenerate is in the fingerbud stage (Fig. 2-12). Electron microscopic and immunochemical studies have detected differentiating muscle proteins

---

Fig. 2-9 (*continued*). small Golgi complex. The muscle fiber is enclosed in a sheath of basement membrane material (sl) which was once termed the sarcolemma but is no longer considered to be part of the cell membrane. In this micrograph, the dedifferentiating cells are pulling away from the connective tissue sheath (sl). The sheath seems to be resorbed subsequently. The multinucleated muscle fiber has cleaved into mononucleate cells, one of which is labeled (N). The tissue illustrated is from the proximal region of an adult *Triturus* limb 18 days after amputation. The changes that occur in the amputated larval limb are similar but take place more quickly. × 10,000.

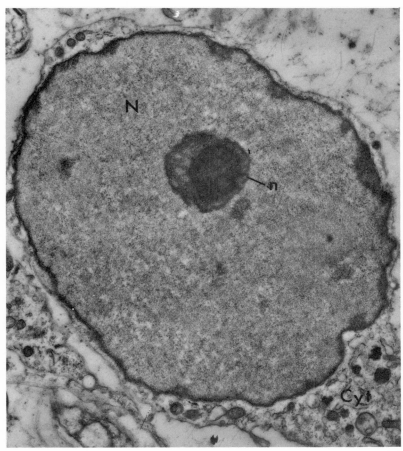

Fig. 2-10. Electron micrograph of a blastema cell in a larval *Ambystoma* limb regenerate. The nucleus (N) is large with highly dispersed chromatin and one or two prominent nucleoli (n). The cytoplasm (Cyt) tends to be scanty and contains free ribonucleoprotein granules, mitochondria, granular and agranular endoplasmic reticulum. The blastema cells are similar in morphology regardless of their tissue of origin. No formed products, such as myofibrils, remain and the cells can be said to be relatively simplified or relatively undifferentiated in appearance. The cells are geared for the synthesis of new RNA and DNA. The resultant proliferation leads to the appearance of a bud of new tissue on the cut end of the limb. Singer (1952) suggested the term "mesenchymatous" to describe this new tissue. We have used the terms "mesenchymatous" and "mesenchymal" interchangeably in the text. × 10,000.

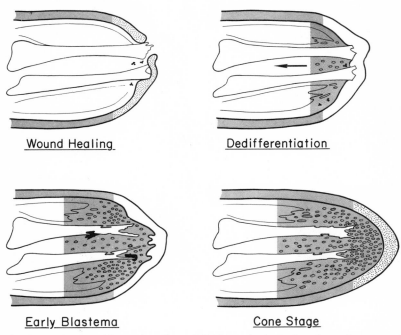

Wound Healing

Dedifferentiation

Early Blastema

Cone Stage

Fig. 2-11. Diagrams illustrating sites of DNA synthesis during the early stages of regeneration of the adult *Triturus* limb. Stippled tissues contain cells that incorporate tritiated thymidine. On the day after amputation (upper left), there is as yet no incorporation of tritiated thymidine in the inner stump tissues. The distal epithelium which has migrated from the stump to cover the wound ceases the DNA synthesis that normally characterizes epidermis. Within 4–5 days, the inner tissues at the cut end of the stump begin to dissociate and these dedifferentiating cells synthesize DNA (upper right). The wave of dedifferentiation of inner tissues (arrow) spreads for a considerable distance proximally during the next 10 days. At 18 days after amputation (lower left), numerous mesenchymal (mesenchymatous) cells occupy the region formerly filled by the differentiated tissues. Much of the bone has been resorbed with the help of osteoclasts (depicted as solid black cells). The apical wound epithelium is thicker due to the distal migration of cells produced in the proximal epidermis where DNA synthesis is very active. Three to four weeks after amputation (lower right), the blastema grows out, taking the shape of a small cone at first. Some DNA synthesis is now detectable in the apical epithelium, but the most active growth centers are still located proximally. Autoradiographic studies of the distribution of incorporated tritiated thymidine fully support the classical work on mitotic indices published by D. T. Chalkley in 1954 and 1959. (After E. D. Hay and D. A. Fischman, 1961.)

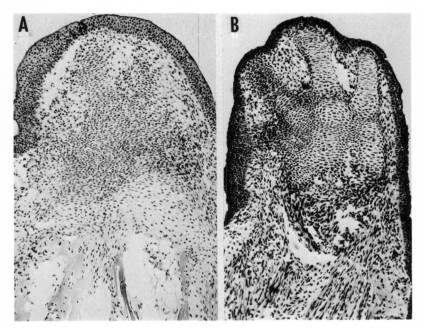

Fig. 2-12. Redifferentiation of the limb regenerate of the adult newt, *Triturus*. (*A*). The growing bud of tissue becomes more flattened in shape when pre-cartilage cells line up to form the skeletal anlage toward the end of the fourth week. The regenerate is referred to as a paddle or palette. (*B*) By 4–5 weeks after amputation of the adult limb, differentiation of the regenerate has advanced to the fingerbud stage. The carpals, phalanges, and other skeletal elements are represented by cartilaginous models which will not ossify until the limb has grown to its original size several months later. Muscle differentiation has barely begun 4–5 weeks after amputation. × 40.

as early as the paddle stage, but the bulk of the new muscle appears later (see Hay, 1962).

The blastema that forms on the adult newt limb is never as large, relative to the rest of the limb, as the blastema of the larval salamander limb. From 2 to 3 weeks are required merely to reach the cone stage, whereas the larval regenerate is actively growing before the end of the first week and has redifferentiated by 2 weeks (Butler, 1933; Chalkley, 1959). The period of proliferation of relatively undifferentiated mesenchymatous cells (cone stage) is extremely short in both cases and is a critical one for the success of the regenerative process (Singer and Craven, 1948). Perhaps because of the slowness of the process of blastema formation in the adult and the brevity of the period of proliferation during the cone stage, earlier workers concluded that the blastema formed without mitosis. Chalkley's exacting analysis of mitotic indices in regenerating limbs of newts demonstrated that mitosis occurs in all of the inner stump tissues *during* the process of dedifferentiation, before and during the so-called phase of active outgrowth (Chalkley, 1959). In autoradiographic studies using tritiated thymidine, it is possible to detect DNA synthesis in nuclei within the muscle, periosteum nerve sheaths, and loose connective tissue of the adult limb 4 days after amputation (Hay and Fischman, 1961). In general, studies of DNA synthesis fail to support the idea of a distal growth center (Faber, 1962). Rather, they tend to emphasize the amazing degree to which the growth processes extend proximally (Figs. 2-11, 2-13, and 2-14) and they call attention to a possible distal shift of material during limb development.

ROLE OF THE WOUND EPITHELIUM

It has been clearly established that a wound epithelium in close contact with the blastema is a requisite for regeneration of the limb. The wound epithelium derives initially by migration of proximal epithelial cells over the cut surface of the stump. The proximal epithelium continues to migrate distally until there is, in the adult newt, a fairly large pile at the tip of the limb (Fig. 2-15). As in the case in all of the higher vertebrates, the cells at the margin of the wound proliferate to replenish the migrating epithelial cells. There is little or no DNA synthesis in the apical cap during the stage of early blastema formation (Hay and Fischman, 1961). The difference between incorporation of tritiated thymidine in the proximal border of the cap and the apical cap itself is striking, even though these cells are adjacent to each other and receive the same blood supply (Fig. 2-16). It would seem as if the migrating cells, once they have started to move, cease to synthesize DNA, although they may complete a mitotic cycle that was underway after they arrive at their destination.

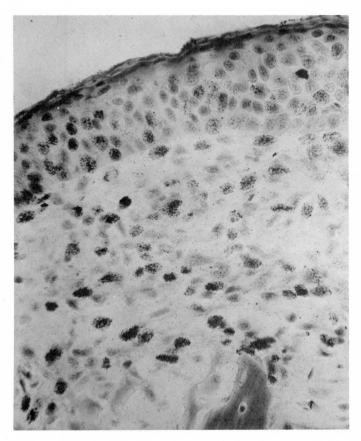

Fig. 2-13. Autoradiograph illustrating the pattern of tritiated thymidine incorporation in a regenerate at the cone stage. The more proximally located blastema cells display the greatest radioactivity, a fact which supports Singer's contention that DNA synthesis normally is stimulated by the nerve or some other agent within the limb, rather than by some agent emitted by the apical epithelium. The slightly labeled distal cells were probably at the end of the DNA synthetic period when the first injection of tritiated thymidine was given 6 hours earlier (see Hay and Fischman, 1961). They may have migrated from, or been pushed forward by, the active proximal growth centers. The regenerate illustrated is that of an adult newt limb 24 days after amputation. × 200.

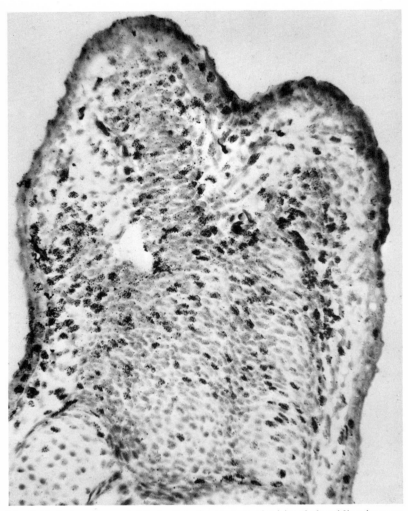

Fig. 2-14. Autoradiograph illustrating the pattern of tritiated thymidine incorporation in a regenerate at the fingerbud stage. Here again, the proximal blastema is more radioactive than the distal or apical regions. There are, however, fewer cells synthesizing DNA in the center than in the periphery of the differentiating cartilaginous mass. The cells comprising the periphery are relatively less differentiated than the cells in the center of the cartilage. At this stage of development, all of the cells are actively synthesizing RNA and protein. The regenerate illus-

The exact function of the apical epithelial cap is not known, although it has been the subject of much study. It seems unlikely that the apical cap actually gives rise to the blastema cells, as proposed by Godlewski, Rose, and others. The apical epithelium does not exhibit the morphological and metabolic characteristics of the dedifferentiating inner tissues (loss of cytoplasmic fibrils and other differentiated structures; increased cytoplasmic basophilia; intense nucleic acid synthesis). Most of the evidence which Rose, Hay, and others presented earlier in support of the idea that epithelial cells enter the blastema (see the review by Rose, 1964) is invalidated by subsequent studies demonstrating the possible distal migration of proximal inner cells (Hay and Fischman, 1961). Studies of mitotic indices and cells labeled with tritiated thymidine give good support to the widely held opinion that the blastema itself normally derives only from the dedifferentiating inner stump tissues (Chalkley, 1959; Hay and Fischman, 1961; but see Rose, 1964). These proliferating mesenchymal cells are more sensitive to x-ray (Stinson, 1958) and actinomycin treatment than the apical cap epithelial cells. Indeed, actinomycin can prevent blastema formation without affecting the development of the epidermal cap (Wolsky and Van Doi, 1965).

Rose (1948) stressed the close contact of the apical epithelium with the blastema and noted that some of the inner cells seemed to project into the blastema, as if to enter it to become blastema cells. Another interpretation of the inward projecting tongues of epithelial cells is that they engulf debris within the wound and aid in exteriorizing it. Singer and Salpeter (1961), Bodemer (1958), and Ide-Rozas (1936) have noted that foreign particles (for example, charcoal) placed under the epithelium are removed through the epithelium. The inward projecting tongues of epidermal cells seem to engulf the particles and exteriorize them, perhaps with the help of the macrophages in the area. In the limbs of adult newts, the apical epithelium has a tendency to pile up around the cut ends of bones and may aid in their removal. The cap is best developed in

---

trated is that of an *Ambystoma* larva fixed 14 days after amputation, 1 hour after administration of tritiated thymidine to the animal. The stage is comparable to that reached by the adult regenerate (Fig. 2-12, *B*) 4–5 weeks after amputation. (From E. D. Hay in *Organogenesis*, edited by R. L. DeHaan and H. Ursprung, Copyright by Holt, Rinehart and Winston, 1965.)

limbs which have not been trimmed flat at the surface after amputation (Fig. 2-15).

Proteolytic or histolytic enzymes may be present in the apical epithelium at the time the cap is prominent, that is, during the

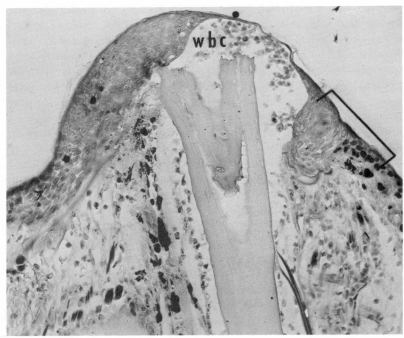

Fig. 2-15. Apical wound epithelium of the limb of adult *Triturus*, 8 days after amputation. The proximal inner tissues contracted slightly after amputation, exposing the cut ulna (shown here) and radius. The epithelium has piled up around the exposed cut bones and finally has closed the wound. White blood cells (wbc) are normally seen during the initial period of wound healing, their number depending on the degree of infection and trauma. Subsequently, osteoclasts that seem to be derived from monocytes appear around the bone and much of the osseous matrix is resorbed. The apical cap persists as a mound of epithelium 12 or more layers in thickness until the cone stage (Fig. 2-11), when it thins out. The figure shown is an autoradiograph. The area indicated by the bracket is shown at higher magnification in the following figure. × 90. (From a photomicrograph by E. D. Hay and D. A. Fischman that originally appeared in *Devel. Biol.*, 1961, 3: 33.)

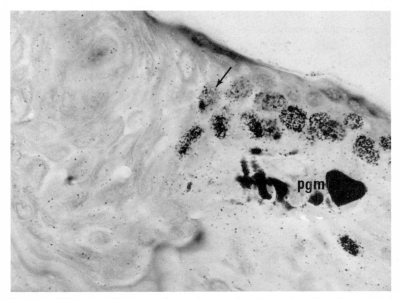

Fig. 2-16. High-magnification photomicrograph of the junction between the apical cap and proximal epithelium, 8 days after amputation. The regenerating limb from which this section was taken was fixed several hours after the newt received tritiated thymidine (Fig. 2-15). The sections were processed for autoradiography and at this magnification the silver grains in the overlying emulsion are clearly visible (arrow). The large, dark clumps under the proximal epithelium are pigmented dermal cells (pgm). Interestingly enough, the apical wound epithelium (to the left) does not synthesize DNA, even though it may contain mitotic figures. The cells in mitosis synthesized DNA in a growth zone located proximal to the cut surface (to the right). Over 30 percent of the cells in the epidermis around the margin of the wound incorporate tritiated thymidine (as opposed to 15 percent in epidermis elsewhere). When these proximal cells migrate distally, they seem to become more differentiatel in the sense that they stop synthesizing DNA, acquire proteolytic and histolytic enzymes, and probably play a role in removal of wound debris. They continue to synthesize RNA (Hay, 1965, Chapter 4). × 350. (From a photomicrograph by E. D. Hay and D. A. Fischman that originally appeared in *Devel. Biol.,* 1961, 3: 33.)

period of dedifferentiation and blastema formation (see Ide-Rozas, 1936; Singer and Salpeter, 1961; Schmidt and Weary, 1963). It is possible that whenever a competent wound epithelium comes in contact with naked connective tissue, it produces enzymes that aid in breaking down collagen fibrils and connective tissue matrix (see Gross, 1964). Indeed, it is only in those animals with well-developed collagenous components (connective tissue, bone), that the apical cap is dramatic in size and configuration (adult salamanders, frogs). The limb of the young *Ambystoma* larva has little connective tissue, no bone, less histolysis and inflammation, less debris, and normally never shows projecting inward tongues of apical epithelium. Along these lines, it is interesting to recall that the tip of the regenerating intestine (Fig. 2-2) is able to initiate histolysis in any organ that it touches (O'Steen, 1958).

It is tempting to think that, in addition to a possible role in histolysis and removal of tissue debris during blastema formation, the apical cap has a function in promoting limb outgrowth. In the larval salamander, the apical epithelium closely resembles the slightly thickened apical ridge of the developing embryonic limb. Thornton (1960) has shown that the orientation of the inner tissues of the regenerating *Ambystoma* limb may be changed completely by moving the apical epithelial cap to one side. Indeed, if the cap faces the lateral surface, the new limb grows out at right angles to the axis of the old stump. In a normally regenerating salamander limb, sensory nerves grow into the apical cap epithelium and establish a close relation with the cells, although their presence within the epithelium is not absolutely requisite for regeneration (see Singer and Inoue, 1964). Is it possible that nerves guided blastema cells toward the apical cap in the experiment quoted above? Thornton and Steen (1962) undertook to study the question in aneurogenic limbs. Nerves are not necessary for embryonic limb development, but they must be present in the stump for regeneration to occur. If a salamander limb is prevented from ever receiving a nerve supply, however, it does not become dependent on nerves in this way. Such aneurogenic limbs regenerate (Yntema, 1959). Thornton and Steen raised aneurogenic larvae, amputated their limbs, shifted the position of the apical caps, and found that the apical epithelium still determined the position of the blastema, even in the absence of nerves. Interestingly enough, skin from a normal animal transplanted to the aneurogenic limb is unable to support regeneration. Once epithelium is dependent on nerve, then, it cannot support limb regeneration in the absence of nerves. Mesodermal tissues, even if previously innervated, however, can be stimulated to grow by the noninnervated epidermis of an aneurogenic limb (Steen and Thornton, 1963). These provocative results do not negate a role of nerves in directing blastema formation under normal conditions, but they do show that the apical cap also has the ability to promote the outgrowth of the regenerate under certain conditions.

ROLE OF NERVES AND HORMONES

If we turn now to consider the role of hormones in limb regeneration, we shall see that just as cells become dependent on nerves during development, so do they come to need certain endocrine secretions. Schotté reported in 1926 that regeneration of limbs does not occur in adult newts in the absence of pituitary, yet he found that larval salamanders are able to regenerate following hypophysectomy. It would seem that the pituitary of the larval salamander has not yet begun to function; at least, not in the sense that it produces the hormones upon which growth of the adult limb is dependent (see Schotté, 1961; Schotté and Hall, 1952). Interestingly enough, the cells of larval *Ambystoma* do not respond to precocious treatment with pituitary substances by losing their regenerative capacities permanently. Thyroid hormones administered to a frog tadpole do permanently inhibit limb regeneration, but, of course, the animal metamorphoses to an adult in the meantime and the adult cannot regenerate. Thyroxine has no permanent effect on salamander regeneration, but if administered during the most critical period of proliferation it retards limb regeneration.

In his studies on the role of the pituitary in adult newts, Schotté has taken the view that ACTH acting on the adrenal cortex is the essential hypophyseal hormone needed for regeneration. Failure of the hypophysectomized adult newt to regenerate is attributed to its failure to react properly to stress (see Schotté, 1961, for review of the work). It was thought that the adrenal corticosteroids which seem to relieve the inhibition prevented formation of thick fibrous tissue on the limb stump in the hypophysectomized newt. Wilkerson (1963) has concluded that this fibrous pad is not a barrier to regeneration, since growth hormone administered to hypophysectomized animals causes regeneration even if given 15 days after amputation, when the fibrous pad has already formed. Interestingly enough, hypophysectomy does not interfere with lens regeneration. Limb regeneration in the adult salamander, however, is as adversely affected by overdoses of hormones as by their absence (see review by Rose, 1964). A real understanding of the relation between endocrine balance and regeneration in amphibians cannot be achieved until the total picture of endocrine function in these animals has been clarified by further physiological studies.

We have already alluded to the dependency of limb regeneration in the adult salamander on a definite threshold of innervation under normal circumstances. The threshold concept derives from the work of Singer in the period 1942–1946, although the importance of innervation to regeneration had been discovered much earlier by Schotté, Todd, and others (see review by Singer, 1952). Earlier investigators were undecided as to whether the sensory nerve supply was more important than the motor and sympathetic supply or vice versa, but Singer showed that the actual number of nerve fibers present is the only determining factor. The sensory supply is normally the largest, but if the motor supply is augmented by additional motor nerves the limb can regenerate without sensory nerves. The direction of conduction is unimportant. Indeed, nerves do not need to be connected to the central nervous system to support regeneration. The number of nerves needed can be influenced, however, by transplanting the limb to another location, such as the back. The threshold requirement probably varies with the capacity of the wound tissue to respond to the nerve (see discussions by Singer, 1952; Singer, 1960; Zika and Singer, 1965).

Investigators have searched for a chemical that might be emitted by the nerve, which would be the factor essential to regeneration. Drugs which block the action of acetylcholine have been infused into regenerates and indeed, substances such as atropine do suppress growth. Acetylcholine, however, is clearly not the chemical substance responsible for the neuronal influence on growth (see Singer, 1960). The science of neuropharmacology is advancing so rapidly today, it is conceivable that future investigations will unveil the true neural substance. Parker (1932) speculated that all neurons might produce trophic neurohumoral substances which radiate along the fibers irrespective of the direction of conduction to promote growth of innervated parts. Growth is most active in the areas of the blastema that are most heavily innervated.

The individual nerve axons come into close contact with the blastema cells (see Singer, 1952; Salpeter, 1965).

The possibility that the nerve action is essentially a stimulatory effect on cell proliferation is reinforced by the fact that the most critical time in terms of dependency on nerve is the period of initial outgrowth of the limb. Regeneration can proceed without innervation once the initial outgrowth is definitely under way (Schotté and Butler, 1944). Denervation of the regenerating larval *Ambystoma* limb at late as 5 days postamputation results in regression of the limb. When the cone stage is reached, the limb varies in its response, but when it has entered the stage of early redifferentiation (paddle stage) it is more stable. Denervation at this time may retard growth, but the limb does not regress (Butler and Schotté, 1949).

The adult *Triturus* limb differs from the larval limb in several respects. It has fewer nerves per unit area (Peadon and Singer, 1965), more connective tissue and bone, and a thicker epidermis. It does not regress following denervation. If the brachial nerves are cut prior to amputation or as late as 13 days after amputation (Fig. 2-17), regeneration is suppressed and a fibrous pad forms over the end of the cut surface (Singer and Craven, 1948). When denervation is delayed until 15 days, the limbs continue to grow but are heteromorphic in some cases. Denervation at 17 days or later (cone to paddle stages) results in normal regenerates that are smaller than they should be.

The type of suppression of regeneration observed after hypophysectomy also varies depending on the time the operation is performed. Complete absence of regeneration was observed only in animals allowed to regenerate 6 days or less prior to hypophysectomy (Schotté and Hall, 1952). The operation may be delayed until 13 days and yet some effect on regeneration, such as heteromorphic growth, will be noted in cases. Pituitary replacement therapy and adrenal corticosteroids are said to be most effective 15 days after amputation. It may be possible, then, that the primary effect of hypophysectomy is not on wound healing so much as it is on cell proliferation. One might interpret the differing effects of denervation and hypophysectomy at different stages (Fig. 2-17) by postulating that not enough new cells have been produced before the early cone stage to allow normal progression of regeneration.

	STAGE TREATMENT BEGUN		
FINAL EFFECT	0-10 Days	10-20 Days	21+ Days
	Wound Healing, Dedifferentiation	Cone Stage Beginning	Paddle Stage
1. Regeneration Suppressed	Hypophysectomy (6 days)	Denervation (13 days)	
2. Abnormal Differentiation		Hypophysectomy (13 days) Denervation (15 days)	
3. Normal, but Small			Hypophysectomy Denervation

Fig. 2-17. Effect on regeneration of denervation and hypophysectomy at different times after amputation. There are three possible levels of inhibition of limb regeneration: (1) complete suppression of regeneration, which usually is expressed in the case of the adult newt by scarring over of the cut stump with no outgrowth (above) and in the larva by regression of the whole limb; (2) partial suppression of regeneration, accompanied by heteromorphic or abnormal differentiation of cartilages and other limb components; (3) partial suppression of regeneration, accompanied by normal limb pattern, but small size. For complete suppression of regeneration, it is necessary to hypophysectomize the adult newt within 6 days after limb amputation (Schotté and Hall, 1952). Even then, some of these cases escape to the second level (heteromorphosis). The latest time after amputation at which hypophysectomy can result in partial suppression of regeneration is 13 days, the beginning of the most active growth period. Denervation of the adult newt limb seems to have a more direct effect and may be delayed as late as 13 days after amputation with complete suppression of regeneration resulting (Singer and Craven, 1948). Most limbs denervated after 15 days, however, proceed to level 3. In all cases, slowing of growth is noted. The results can be interpreted in terms of a direct (denervation) or indirect (hypophysectomy) effect on cell proliferation. The abnormal pattern of cartilage differentiation (level 2) may result when an insufficient mass of cells is produced to faithfully form the entire limb.

74

Yet enough cells have been produced by the paddle stage to insure redifferentiation of the limb pattern. The heteromorphic growths (Fig. 2-17) may result because an insufficient mass of cells is present for correct differentiation of the skeletal pattern (see Bretscher and Tschumi, 1951).

INHIBITION AND INDUCTION
OF LIMB REGENERATION

Most chemical agents which retard amphibian limb regeneration produce the same pattern of abnormalities noted above (Fig. 2-17), although some compounds, such as beryllium, are actually destructive (Scheuing and Singer, 1957). The main effect, directly or indirectly, of many of the chemicals may be to inhibit cell proliferation and in this way to produce heteromorphic growths (Hay, 1956). The primary cytological effect of x-ray is depression of cell division (see Das and Alfert, 1961). Metabolic antagonists to protein or nucleic acid synthesis would also be expected to inhibit cell division. Gebhardt and Faber (unpublished observations) have noted heteromorphic regenerates when aminopterin is administered during the cone stage (see also Bieber and Hitchings, 1959). One might speculate again that the atypical cartilage differentiation and incomplete muscle development observed when growth is partially inhibited reflects, directly or indirectly, the failure to produce a large enough cellular mass for proper reformation of limb structures.

Most attempts to induce regeneration in frogs and higher vertebrates have, at best, enhanced the growth potential to the heteromorphic level (Fig. 2-17). Normally an amputated limb scars over with little or no outgrowth in adult *Rana*. Polezhayev discovered that trauma to the cut surface of the amputated limb stump stimulates outgrowth in late tadpoles. Rose extended this approach and used strong salt solutions as a method of providing an initial irritation to the amputated limbs of young adult frogs. The limb outgrowths so induced were invariably heteromorphic and consisted mostly of cartilage, as was true also of frog limbs stimulated to grow by transplants of younger skin or infusions of embryonic materials (see reviews by Polezhayev, 1945, 1946; Rose, 1944, 1964; Bodemer, 1964). Dent (1962) reported heteromorphic growths in *Xenopus laevis* under normal circumstances. Perhaps regeneration in this aquatic anuran could be raised to a level resembling perfect regrowth (Fig. 2-17) by some of the methods which induce heteromorphic growth in *Rana*.

Schotté and Wilber (1958) transplanted adrenal glands to the jaws of young green frogs (*Rana clamitans*) and in most cases obtained some regeneration after amputation through the radius-ulnar region. In the case illustrated (Fig. 2-18), one of the regenerates, 8 months after the operation, showed a new radius-ulna, some carpal formations, and a free digit with phalangeal ossifications. This degree of regeneration, while still heteromorphic, is perhaps the best ever induced from the limb stump of an adult *Rana*. Schotté and Smith (1961) extended this approach to a study of the

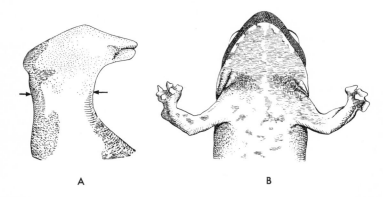

A   B

Fig. 2-18. Heteromorphic regeneration of frog limbs induced by increasing the innervation of the limb (*A*) or by increasing the circulating adrenal hormones (*B*). Normally limbs of adult *Rana* scar over with little or no outgrowth after amputation (Fig. 2-17, level 1). Methods that stimulate increased cell proliferation (see text) can raise the level of regeneration in *Rana,* but in no case has a perfect limb pattern been reproduced. The experiments suggest, however, that the poor ability of frog limbs to regenerate reflects changes in systemic factors rather than changes in the cells per se. (*A*) Regeneration following transplantation of the sciatic nerve to the forelimb of a young grass frog. (After M. Singer, 1954, from a halftone drawing that originally appeared in *J. Exp. Zool.,* **126:** 471.) (*B*) Regeneration of the forelimbs of a young green frog following transplantation of extra adrenal glands to the jaw. (After O. E. Schotté and C. B. Wilber, 1958, from a photograph that originally appeared in *J. Embryol. Exp. Morphol.,* **6:** 247.)

embryonic mouse limb. It was found that ACTH and cortisone delay both epidermal and dermal closure without, however, raising the response to the level of heteromorphic regeneration noted in frogs (see also Scharf, 1961).

Heteromorphic limb regenerates can be induced in *Rana* (Fig. 2-18) and several species of lizards (Fig. 2-19) by augmentation of

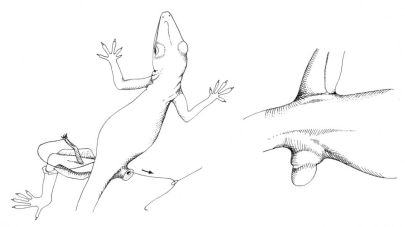

Fig. 2-19. Augmentation of the nerve supply of the lizard hindlimb with subsequent heteromorphic regeneration. The lizard, *Anolis carolinensis*, has fewer peripheral nerves relative to the total mass of the limb than does the frog, and the threshold of cell response to the trophic effect of nerves is higher. Efforts to stimulate regeneration in various lizards (see Zika and Singer, 1965, for review) have barely raised the response to level 2 (Fig. 2-17). In the higher vertebrates, it has not been possible to induce even this much limb regeneration. (After M. Singer, 1961, *Proc. Soc. Exp. Biol. Med.* **107**: 106.)

the nerve supply (see Simpson, 1965; Zika and Singer, 1965). The result is interpreted in terms of a trophic effect exerted by the nerves. The frog and lizard limbs have fewer nerves relative to their size than the salamander. Indeed, there is a definite relation between nerve content and ability to regenerate at various levels of the tadpole hind limb just prior to metamorphosis (Van Stone, 1964). Zika and Singer (1965) suggest that the relative decline in limb innervation in the higher terrestrial vertebrates is correlated with increasing development of the central nervous system, the elaboration of central nervous mechanisms being of more survival value than the rich peripheral innervation needed for regeneration (see also Singer, 1954).

While it is possible that mitotic stimulants or neural trophic substances will be found which are capable of stimulating sufficient cell proliferation to bring about full regeneration of limbs of higher vertebrates, the evolutionary considerations in the first part of the chapter have to be taken into account in any speculation along these lines. The mammal has not "lost" the ability to regenerate organs such as the liver. The higher vertebrates have evolved more specialized and abundant connective tissues than occur in amphibians and, at the same time, have developed wound-healing mechanisms which, although they seem less dramatic in terms of the appendage itself, are nevertheless an important adaptation to terrestrial life, as we shall see in the next chapter.

chapter three

Regeneration
in Mammals

PHYSIOLOGICAL REGENERATION

Every vertebrate is dependent to some extent on physiological regeneration for survival and in no case is this better exemplified than in the mammal. One of the distinguishing features of the class is that the members are covered with hair which is periodically molted. The surface epithelium is a stratified epidermis specialized for continuous replacement of cells in the outer, protective layer. A cell in the basal stratum of the multilayered squamous epithelium of the mouse tongue may reach the surface in a little over a week (Leblond *et al.,* 1959). Most of the skin appendages, such as hairs, sebaceous glands, nails, claws, hoofs, scales, and horns, grow continuously or periodically. The antlers of deer, which consist of bone covered initially with a hairy skin, are shed annually and replaced by new growth. The dermis, sometimes considered to be the tissue that inhibits limb regeneration in mammals, does in fact play the most important role in bringing about regeneration of the antler (Goss, 1964a). Teeth, which evolved from placoid scales such as occur in sharks, are lost and replaced continuously in lower vertebrates, but in mammals they are more specialized and are shed once, then replaced by a permanent set. If the roots remain open, however, the teeth may continue to grow for the life of the animal (rodents).

Autoradiographic studies using tritiated thymidine to label progenitor cells reveal a striking turnover of cells in the intestinal epithelium of mammals and other vertebrates. The cells that are synthesizing DNA are located exclusively in the intestinal crypts of mammals (Fig. 3-1). It can be shown in humans by serial biopsies, that the cells which incorporate tritiated thymidine at the time of administration of the isotope have divided by the next day. A certain percentage then re-enters the mitotic cycle (Fig. 3-2). The

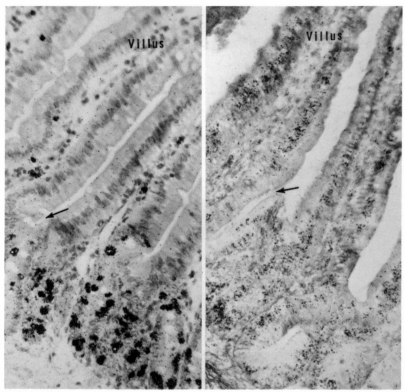

Fig. 3-1. Autoradiographs of mouse intestine. On the left is a section of tissue from an animal fixed a few hours after injection of tritiated thymidine. The tissue on the right is from an animal fixed 30 hours after injection of tritiated thymidine. All of the cells that synthesize DNA are located in the intestinal crypts (below the arrow, on the left). By the day following injection, these cells have divided, thus diluting the label incorporated at the time of injection. A significant number of cells have moved out of the crypts along the villi at this time (above the arrow, on the right). × 200.

remainder move up the villi, differentiating into absorptive cells along the way. The entire epithelium of each villus turns over every 2–3 days (Quastler and Sherman, 1959; Leblond, 1965). It has been estimated that the rate of cell movement is one cell position per hour along the villus. The mechanisms by which the cells

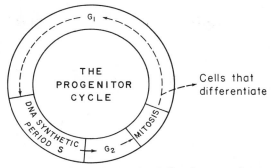

Fig. 3-2. Diagram of the progenitor cycle. Cells of a renewing population are remarkably constant in the time required for DNA synthesis (the S period). Mouse epithelial cells such as illustrated in the preceding figure spend 7 hours duplicating their DNA in interphase. There is a variable gap (G_2) of an hour or more between the end of DNA synthesis and the beginning of mitosis. RNA synthesis is known to continue during this time. Mitosis (prophase, metaphase, anaphase, telophase) usually requires 1 hour. A period of interphase (G_1) now ensues during which there is no DNA synthesis. RNA and protein synthesis may be very active during G_1. G_1 averages 10 hours, about half of the total progenitor time in a renewing cell population. Cells that differentiate often move out of the progenitor cycle and remain in interphase until their demise, a period of 46 hours in the case of the differentiating intestinal epithelial cell. (After I. L. Cameron and R. C. Greulich, *J. Cell Biol.*, 1963, **18:** 33.)

move out to certain death at the tip of the villus and the reasons for the limited life cycle are poorly understood (see Gelfant, 1963). Presumably, such a regular turnover insures against possible loss of the simple epithelium through wear and tear.

Quantitative studies employing cell and grain counts in tissues fixed at different intervals after isotope administration make it possible to estimate the time a cell spends in each phase of the progenitor (mitotic) cycle (Lamerton and Fry, 1963; Cameron and Greulich, 1963). The duration of the phase of DNA synthesis (the S phase) for most somatic cells is 6–8 hours. Not all of the chromosomes are replicated at the same time. Thus, the intensity of tritiated thymidine incorporation varies from moment to moment, and probably is at its lowest peak toward the end of the S phase. It would seem that the sex chromosomes are among the last to replicate (Hsu *et al.*, 1964). There is usually a short (1–2 hours) period between the end of DNA synthesis and actual cell division. This period, known as gap 2 (G2), may be characterized by continuing RNA and protein synthesis (Prescott, 1964). Mitosis per se requires about an hour. The cells in the intestinal crypt must then make a decision as to whether to re-enter the progenitor cycle or move out to differentiate into absorptive and glandular cells. If they move out of the crypt, the period of their last interphase is 46 hours in the mouse, the time required to reach the sloughing zone at the tip of a villus. If, however, they re-enter the progenitor cycle, interphase (G1) averages 10 hours, then DNA synthesis (S phase) re-ensues. The controlling mechanisms for this process are so exact that a balance between progenitor cycle and differentiation is attained which keeps the intestinal mucosa continuously clothed with a marching carpet of millions of absorptive and secretory cells.

The processes by which the blood is renewed continuously are not any less dramatic. In the human, some 100 billion granulocytes are produced in the bone marrow and squandered each day in the continuing battle against bacteria and other foreign organisms. This figure does not include the additional millions of monocytes and lymphocytes which emerge from lymphatic centers all over the body daily to transform into macrophages, plasma cells, and so on. Nor does it include the short-lived, anucleate red blood cell. The total production of various blood cells daily is in order of 300×10^9 cells per 70 Kg man (Galbraith *et al.*, 1965).

There are two principal progenitor cycles in the bone marrow, the erythropoietic which seems to be under the control of circulating substances such as erythropoietin (see Goss, 1964b), and the granulocytic (myeloid) series. The progenitor cells of the two series fall into three main groups or "compartments" in the marrow:

(1) The reticular cells, once thought of as stem cells. Normally these cells probably play a supportive rather than a progenitor role in blood cell development. They are stimulated to divide by blood loss, infection, and other trauma.

(2) The young blood cells of the erythropoietic series (proerythroblasts, erythroblasts) and granulocytic series (promyelocytes, myelocytes). These are the only cells which incorporate tritiated thymidine under normal conditions. They comprise about 25 percent of the bone marrow population. The autoradiographic studies emphasize the surprising fact that these partially differentiated

cells, not the reticular cells, normally perpetuate the marrow population (Cartwright *et al.*, 1964; Cronkite and Fliedner, 1964).

(3) Red and white blood cells that have almost completed their maturation (normoblasts, metamyelocytes). These cells do not incorporate tritiated thymidine. They are almost fully mature and soon will be released into the circulation.

Not only have autoradiographic studies changed the older concepts about the role of reticular cells in blood regeneration, but they also have destroyed the myth that a cancer cells grows as fast as an early embryonic cell. The normal hamster cheek pouch epithelium has an S period of 10 hours and a total cell cycle of 142 hours. It has been shown that the S period in the hamster cheek pouch carcinoma is 6–7 hours and the total mitotic cycle is 20 hours. Moreover, in many tumors less than half the cells are growing. The damage produced by the malignant cells results from the uncontrolled nature of their growth, the lack of an orderly cycle of maturation, migration, and destruction (Reiskin and Mendelsohn, 1964). The most clear-cut case of significant shortening of the S phase in vertebrates is to be found not in somatic cells, but in the highly specialized developing oöcytes. During early cleavage of the *Xenopus* egg, the S phase requires only 10 minutes and the whole progenitor cycle, less than 15 minutes. At gastrulation the S period is about 1 hour; it slows to 5 hours in the mid neurula (Graham and Morgan, 1966). The short progenitor cycle in early cleavage is accomplished by eliminating G1, shortening G2 and M and by utilizing stored precursors during the S phase.

As we have seen in previous chapters, dividing cells are very sensitive to ionizing radiation. X-irradiation in low dosage does not inhibit DNA synthesis markedly, but it may block the transition from G1 to S or from G2 to M (Elkind *et al.*, 1963; Puck and Steffen, 1963.). Ionizing radiation produces damage to the intact animal by interfering with physiological regeneration of blood cells and epithelium (Patt and Quastler, 1963). The fatal symptoms of massive body irradiation are caused by bone marrow failure and rapid denudation of the intestinal epithelium. The replacement of other epithelial tissues and the production of germ cells also are affected, of course, but only become important to consider in chronic cases involving smaller amounts of radiation.

The cells of the adult body can be divided into three main

groups depending on the degree to which they normally are growing or turning over:

(1) The labile (renewing) group, consists of blood cells and surface epithelia. There is always a well-defined progenitor cycle and the cells in the growth zone are only partially differentiated (stratum germinativum of skin, crypt cells of intestine, myelocytes, erythroblasts). The medium-sized and large lymphocytes, which are the mononucleated white blood cells of the lymph nodules that incorporate tritiated thymidine, normally are committed to produce plasma cells, macrophages, and small lymphocytes. Certain connective tissue cells, such as mast cells, might also be classified as labile, although their progenitor cell has not been clearly defined. The end-product cell of the renewing group is terminally differentiated and dispensable.

(2) The stable (expanding) group were characterized by Leblond *et al.* (1959) as showing some tritiated thymidine incorporation in the adult. These are the epithelial and connective tissue merocrine gland cells, such as occur in liver, kidney, pancreas, cartilages, and loose connective tissue. The end-product cell is not necessarily terminal and the cell population may expand under stress.

(3) The static (permanent) group show no cell division in the normal adult. These are the muscle and nerve cells. They are capable of hypertrophy in response to stress, but do not normally show hyperplasia. Tissues composed of such cells have little or no capacity for regeneration after massive injury.

REPARATIVE REGENERATION

The renewing surface epithelia of the body are capable of repairing wounds of considerable size after a variety of accidents, such as burns, abrasions, and cuts. The process of epidermal healing when the skin is cut or surgically excised will be considered below under a separate heading. The corneal epithelium has the ability to migrate very rapidly over a denuded surface (Johnson and McMinn, 1960). Homografts of cornea take very well because of the lack of vascularization and immune response and are eventually repopulated by cells of the host. In mammals, such as the rabbit, lens epithelium has some ability to regenerate (Harding and Srinivasan,

1961). The regenerative ability of the urinary bladder, gall bladder, and intestine have been demonstrated repeatedly (see Goss, 1964). The type of healing and proliferation that occurs periodically during the menstrual cycle in the primate might be classified as reparative as well as physiological regeneration. A number of hormones and complex controlling mechanisms are involved in the cyclic processes.

The ability of the hemopoietic tissues to regenerate has been used to advantage in modern surgery. It has been possible to transplant organs, such as the kidney, between genetically different individuals of the same species (homografts). In the pioneering work along these lines, hemopoietic tissue of the host was suppressed prior to the operation by total body irradiation, with the idea that all of the new lymphoid cells would develop in the presence of the graft. The regenerated cells, like embryonic blood cells, would be expected to be tolerant to the foreign graft, so that fatal immune responses are avoided (Billingham, 1964). Currently, drugs rather than irradiation are more often used to suppress the immunological response after surgery employing homografts (Russell and Monaco, 1964).

Among the so-called stable group of cells, the ability of epithelial glands to regenerate is particularly notable. The liver of the rodent, which normally is growing to some extent, has been investigated most extensively, but it is clear that the human liver, too, has remarkable powers of recuperation. If the liver is massively damaged or partially excised (three quarters of the rat liver can be removed), the first observed change in the remaining liver cells is an increase in RNA and protein synthesis. Enzymes (for example, thymidylic kinase) related to DNA synthesis make their appearance. The cells might be said to have entered the G1 phase of the progenitor cycle. In the case of rat liver, 30 percent of the remaining liver cells have begun to synthesize DNA at 20 hours. At 26 hours, the mitotic index reaches a peak (3.6 percent of the cells are in mitosis). Proliferation soon slows, presumably under the influence of humoral factors, so that by 3 days only 3 percent of the cells are synthesizing DNA (Bucher, 1963; Grisham, 1962; Shea, 1964). So rigid are the control mechanisms, that the liver never overshoots its original size during regeneration (see discussion of compensatory hyperplasia by Goss, 1964b). Interestingly enough, the proliferating liver cells do not seem to dedifferentiate. Presumably, the period of maximal cell division (1–2 days) is attained so readily and is so short in duration, that the rather stable differentiated cytoplasmic organelles and ribosomes of the liver cell persist in spite of the fact that metabolism has shifted temporarily to DNA synthesis.

The fibrocytes, chondrocytes, and osteocytes that secreted the connective tissue matrix are, in most mammals, rather quiescent after the animal reaches maturity. The nucleus of the cell is usually fairly condensed and the cytoplasm is scanty or empty appearing. In order for significant growth to ensue, the tissue must dedifferentiate in the sense that a certain amount of the confining extracellular matrix must be lysed and new machinery for synthesizing nucleic acids and proteins must be acquired by the cells. If a bone is fractured, for example, the following series of events takes place. Soon after the fracture, there is a certain amount of cell death in the broken ends of the bone and the surrounding tissue due to the interruption in the blood supply. These cells will be lysed and the matrix that surrounded them will eventually be resorbed, as will the blood clot that usually forms around the bone fragments after injury. Within 2–3 days, cells released from the periosteum, endosteum, and perhaps also from the marrow and adjacent connective tissue, begin to proliferate. They form a collar or callus around the ends of the bone which serves as a natural splint to protect the injured site (Fig. 3-3). The length of time required to form the cellular callus, its size, and the extent to which the callus chondrifies prior to ossification depends on the size of the injury, the type of surgical intervention, and other factors (Ham, 1965). The callus is usually chondrified and partially ossified within 2 weeks. Remodeling of the newly formed bone may take years.

Cell dedifferentiation after injury is perhaps most marked in

---

Fig. 3-3 (*Facing page*). Healing of a bone fracture. The drawing at the top illustrates the formation of the protective external connective tissue callus around the broken end of the bone. Differentiation of new internal osseous trabeculae (black) from the proliferating endosteum and marrow cells has begun. The trabeculae will form the internal callus that more firmly unites the cut edges of the bone (lower drawing). The osteocytes near the cut end of the bone die due to the injury to their Haversian systems. After the new osseous trabeculae form, the dead bone will gradually dissolve away. Trabeculae in the periphery of the bone fill in to form compact osseous tissue and eventually the extraneous

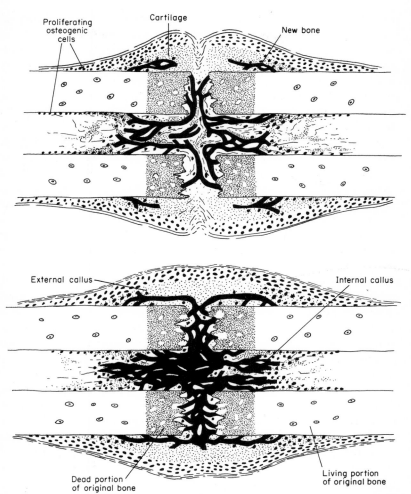

Proliferating osteogenic cells

Cartilage

New bone

External callus

Internal callus

Dead portion of original bone

Living portion of original bone

trabeculae of the internal callus will disappear. The external callus originates primarily by proliferation of osteogenic cells of the periosteum. Its inner, vascularized portion differentiates directly into bony trabeculae that are continuous with the new internal bone. The outer part tends to chondrify. The amount of cartilage in the external callus varies and is greater if there is motion around the break. Eventually, the cartilage calcifies and is replaced by osseous tissue which subsequently undergoes remodeling and resorption as the fracture heals and the original form of the bones is reconstituted. (After A. W. Ham, *Histology*, 1965, by permission of J. B. Lippincott Co.)

muscle which, it will be recalled, consists of static cells. The developmental processes that led to the formation of the multinucleated (syncytial) striated muscle fiber seem to be incompatible with proliferation. An injured muscle fiber always loses cytoplasmic structure and tends to fragment into smaller cellular units. The extent to which the mononucleated cells derived from the fibers are able to divide and join up with similar cells on the other side of the lesion determines the success of the repair (Le Gros Clark, 1946; Jones, 1957; Lash et al., 1957; Bintliff and Walker, 1960; Pietsch, 1961). Thus, if the ends of severed muscle fibers are closely juxtaposed, muscle regeneration in mammals can be excellent. But if the severed ends are separated, the space will fill in with connective (scar) tissue. In the case of cardiac muscle, similar regenerative abilities undoubtedly are present, but are not manifested to a great extent because the injury is usually ischemia. The cells are deprived of the necessary metabolic conditions for growth. Repair processes in smooth (nonstriated) muscle have not been fully clarified in mammals, but in amphibian wound healing, dedifferentiation is involved (see Chapter Two). The smooth muscle of the mammalian uterus is capable of considerable expansion, perhaps due more to cellular hypertrophy than to hyperplasia. In healing after surgical incisions of the uterus, however, new smooth muscle cell formation has been reported (Selye and McKeown, 1934).

The neuron, like the myocyte, is a permanent or static cell type in the normal adult. Even though the cells seemingly exert a trophic action on the growth of other tissues, neurons themselves have no capacity for cell division. The ability of the mammalian neuron to regenerate axons is confined to the peripheral motor and sensory processes. Central neurons are reported to send out cytoplasmic processes after injury to the spinal cord, but these axons do not grow far enough to establish functional continuity within the cord. Failure of complete regeneration of axons in the mammalian central nervous system may be due to the complex arrangement of the neuroglial sheaths. The Schwann cell sheaths that occur around peripheral axons, as we shall see below, have an important role in successful regeneration of these fibers. Interestingly enough, the neurosecretory function of the hypothalamic tract to the pituitary can be restored after transection (Hild and Zetler, 1953).

The ability of sensory and motor nerve cells to regrow their long peripheral processes, which are often a yard or more in length, attests to the considerable synthetic capacity of these enormous neurons. In spite of (or because of) its irreversible commitment to a life without mitosis, the neuron is an exceedingly active interphase cell. The nucleus is large and vesicular, and the nucleolus is prominent. Ergastoplasm and free ribosomes are abundant in the cytoplasm and the Golgi complex is well developed. The membranous organelles probably are involved in neurosecretion, whereas the free ribosomes most likely are synthesizing new proteins to replenish the cytoplasmic processes. Proteinaceous materials flow down the axons at the rate of 1–2 mm a day. A regenerating fiber grows at about the same rate. The flow of protoplasm down the axon can be demonstrated by constricting a regenerating fiber after it has made its connection with the periphery. A bulge will appear on the proximal side of the constriction and there will be no further increase in width on the distal side (Weiss and Hiscoe, 1948).

When a peripheral nerve fiber is crushed severely or cut, the axon distal to the injury degenerates completely. Proximal degeneration of the axon rarely extends past the nearest node of Ranvier. The cell body of the affected axon reacts to the injury in a characteristic fashion. The Nissl bodies undergo *chromatolysis* within 24 hours, that is, the cytoplasm loses the typical basophilic staining reaction, or "color." This "retrograde degenerative process" reaches its maximum in a few days and results in the loss of considerable ergastoplasm. The nucleus and residual Nissl bodies take up an eccentric location in the injured neuron. The nucleolus increases in size and presumably new ribosomes are formed which take part in the protein synthetic processes that must occur if cytoplasmic regeneration is to take place. The neuron does not resume its former state of differentiation for a number of weeks. The distal axon, and myelin sheath if present, have broken up into fragments and droplets during the first few days after injury. This process is called *Wallerian degeneration*. The Schwann cells exhibit acid phosphatase activity and probably take part in the phagocytosis of lysed debris.

As early as 4 days after injury to the nerve, new pseudopodia appear at the cut ends of the axons (Fig. 3-4). They ramify through the surrounding debris, guided by the Schwann cell sheaths, seem-

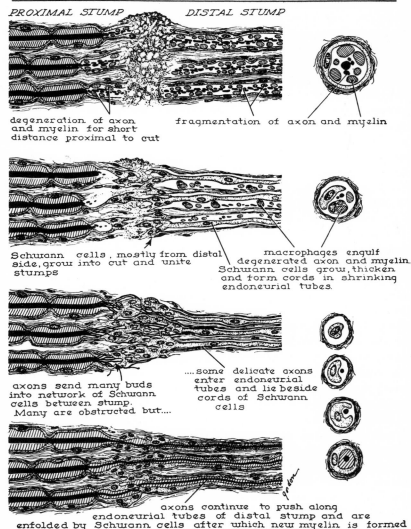

PROXIMAL STUMP　　　　*DISTAL STUMP*

degeneration of axon
and myelin for short
distance proximal to cut

fragmentation of axon and myelin

Schwann cells, mostly from distal
side, grow into cut and unite
stumps

macrophages engulf
degenerated axon and myelin.
Schwann cells grow, thicken
and form cords in shrinking
endoneurial tubes.

axons send many buds
into network of Schwann
cells between stump.
Many are obstructed but....

....some delicate axons
enter endoneurial
tubes and lie beside
cords of Schwann
cells

axons continue to push along
endoneurial tubes of distal stump and are
enfolded by Schwann cells after which new myelin is formed

Fig. 3-4. Regeneration of a peripheral nerve. The injury in this case has completely severed the two ends of the nerves. The gap will be spanned by proliferating cells from the nerve sheaths (Schwann cells). The proximal axons grow into the mazelike area of Schwann cell processes and after probing and branching, traverse the cut to enter the empty distal sheaths. Under the best circumstances, axons will grow down these distal tubes at a rate of 1–2 mm/day. (From A. W. Ham, *Histology*. Philadelphia: J. B. Lippincott Co., 1965.)

ingly moving along the lines of least resistance in the external milieu (contact guidance theory of Weiss, 1955). If the injury is extensive, surgical intervention to join the ends of the nerve is required. Otherwise the fibers will form a useless, sometimes painful neuroma, for lack of a clear-cut path to follow. If a motor fiber by mischance grows down a sensory fiber Schwann sheath, restoration of function is obviously impossible. Relearning of function does not occur very readily even when sensory or motor fibers make smaller errors than this (Sperry, 1959). The total repair process may take months, depending on the problems encountered by the growing nerve fibers (Edds, 1953).

HEALING OF SKIN WOUNDS

Because of the obvious surgical implications, much research has been concerned with the healing of skin wounds. A surgical jargon has arisen which tends to obscure easy comprehension of the basic processes. For example, a considerable amount of attention is given to the difference between first and second intention healing. Wounds that heal by "first intention" are entirely the invention of man. These are sutured incisions with no separation of the edges of the wound, almost no blood clot, no inflammation, and little formation of "granulation" tissue. Epithelization and reunion of the connective tissue components are the main regenerative processes. So-called second intention healing, which will be described below, occurs in a wound with separated edges. Sometimes the term "third intention healing" is used to describe an open wound which is sutured together after it had started to repair itself (Dunphy and Warren, 1963).

The first stage of second intention wound healing in the human is one of demolition and inflammation, accompanied by signs of proliferation in the tissues affected by the injury. The inflammatory stage lasts 2–3 days or longer, depending on the degree of infection. The adjacent epithelium, primarily the middle layer, begins almost immediately to migrate in to cover the wound. It does not flow over the top of the blood clot, but plunges beneath the fibrin into the depths of the wound until it meets the dermal connective tissue (Fig. 3-5). Although mitoses are sometimes seen in the migrating epithelium (Johnson and McMinn, 1960), the bulk of the DNA

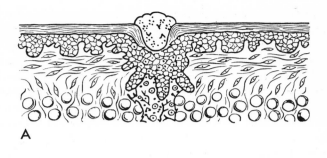

A

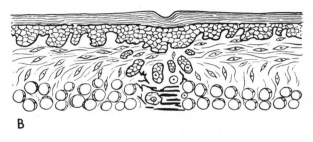

B

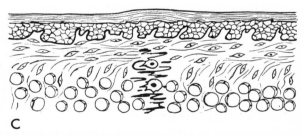

C

Fig. 3-5. Epithelial migration and regression during healing of a cutaneous wound in man, as described by Gillman. Instead of migrating over the surface of the fibrin clot (*A*), the basal layers of the epidermis plunge inward to the dermal connective tissue layer. The wound epidermis thickens due to continuing migration and proliferation (see Chapter Two). With redifferentiation of the dermis and formation of new collagen fibers, isolated epithelial cells break off and are resorbed (*C*), so that the contour of the basal epidermal layers regains its normal appearance. The wound epithelium is rich in phosphatases and may secrete proteolytic enzymes. (After J. E. Dunphy, 1960, from R. Warren, *Surgery*. Philadelphia: W. B. Saunders Co., 1963.)

synthesis or growth seems to be located in cells at the margin of the cut surface, as claimed by earlier workers (Arey, 1936). The wound epithelium thickens and sends irregular processes inward. This thickening does not regress until connective tissue redifferentiation begins and then isolated epithelial cells are said to be pinched off and absorbed (Edwards and Dunphy, 1958; Dunphy and Warren, 1963). The appearance of the epithelium in second intention healing is remarkably similar to that of the wound epithelium of the amputated limb of an adult amphibian. Phosphatases and proteolytic enzymes have been described in the wound epithelium of mammals (Washburn, 1955) as well as amphibians. Here again, perhaps one of its functions is proteolysis and exteriorization of internal debris (see Chapter Two).

If inflammation of the wound is extensive, there may be considerable edema, dilation of underlying capillaries, and exudation of leucocytes and plasma from the vessels. The important role of the lymphatics in removing the debris has recently been documented by Burke, Leak, and Morris (1966). The term "granulation tissue" stems from the gross observation of pink "granules" on the open surface of inflammed wounds (see Dunphy and Warren, 1963). Each granule is a tuft of new blood vessels, fibrin, and young fibroblasts. The new vessels grow in direct continuity with old vessels. Fibroplasia begins at the periphery of the wound when the central portions are still filled with leucocytes. It seems more likely that the growing fibroblasts arose from previously existing connective tissue cells rather than from the leucocytes, but their origin has not gone uncontested (Edwards and Dunphy, 1958). On the sixth or seventh day, microscopically visible collagen fibrils make their appearance, yet collagen secretion may actually begin earlier (Ross, 1964). Reformation of mucopolysaccharides is delayed (Jackson et al., 1960). This second stage of wound healing, fibrosis and completion of epithelization, may last 10 days, but the full tensile strength of the scar does not develop for months.

Wound healing is more rapid in young than in old individuals, but is more easily impeded in the young animal by nutritional deficiencies (vitamin C, protein). Keloids (overgrowths of vascular connective tissue) are most common in young individuals and especially in Negroes. The effect of hormones on mammalian wound healing has been the subject of much research, but the investigations have produced a mass of confusing data (Edwards and Dunphy, 1958). Steroids such as cortisone may decrease the inflammatory action, but they do not seriously impede wound repair unless they are given prior to and during the inflammatory stage. Steroids do not suppress fibroplasia directly and neither adrenalectomy nor hypophysectomy influences repair of mammalian wounds (Dunphy and Warren, 1963). Nor does total body irradiation in association with tissue and organ transplantation significantly inhibit wound repair during the first 2 weeks.

Wound *contraction* is a rather remarkable tissue migration which is particularly well developed in those hairy mammals with a prominent *panniculus carnosus* (superficial striated muscle layer associated with the skin). The wound may spread open to an enormous degree, due to the action of these muscles. A battle wound on the head of a male cat exposing the entire forehead can contract to almost complete closure in a few days. Wound contraction can and does take place in humans, especially over the buttocks, abdominal wall, and neck (Fig. 3-6), but it is slower and does not necessarily involve the same mechanisms as in the experimental

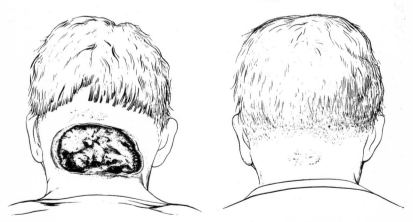

Fig. 3-6. Wound contraction in man. On the left is shown the appearance of a wound on the back of the neck following surgical excision of a large carbuncle. Healing occurred in 2 months, at which time maximum contraction had taken place. Subsidence of edema and redness of the scar took another 4 months. On the right is shown appearance of the wound 6 months after the excision. (From R. Warren, *Surgery*. Philadelphia: W. B. Saunders Co., 1963.)

animals that have been studied (James, 1964). From a study of wound healing in the guinea pig, Watts *et al.* (1958) propose that the machinery for the major part of contraction lies in the connective tissue of the wound margin. Excision of central granulation tissue did not affect contraction, but an excision that included as little as 0.5 mm of the skin margin caused immediate retraction of the wound area to a size greater than the original. Repeated freeing of the edges of the wound completely inhibited contraction. These workers propose that contraction in hairy mammals is due to mass migration of connective tissue cells around the margin of the wound. This is not to say that scab formation and drying in early stages and cicatrization in later stages do not affect the size of the wound, especially in the human. But scar formation is not the principal component of the dramatic contraction observed in these studies. Moreover, wound contraction is also to be distinguished from *contracture,* which is limitation of movement, especially around joints, due to slowly forming scar tissue.

chapter four ▸ Fine Structure

of Regeneration Cells

CELL FINE STRUCTURE AND FUNCTION

One of the surprising revelations of electron microscopic studies of different animals, and plants as well, is the close similarity of organelle fine structure in cells of apparently diverse origin. Thus, we find that mitochondria are all of about the same size and, except for the occasional specializations that are bound to occur, possess the same basic fine structure. There is almost invariably an outer trilaminar phosphoprotein membrane and an inner membrane of similar dimensions which invaginates to form cristae within the mitochondrial matrix. Enzymes involved in oxidative metabolism are believed to be located on the cristae in an orderly array. The organelle called the endoplasmic reticulum is represented in all animals and plants by a granular form (referred to as ergastoplasm if it is abundant) and by a smooth surfaced form (also called agranular reticulum). The granular endoplasmic reticulum is comprised of membrane-bounded cisternae or sacs lined with adherent ribosomes. The cavity may seem to be empty, but on occasion is found to be filled with secretory materials. One of the functions of the granular reticulum is the synthesis and partitioning of proteins destined for the extracellular compartment (Fig. 4-1).

The smooth-surfaced reticulum is an ubiquitous organelle which must have a diversity of functions. The membranes that line the various vesicles, tubules, and cisternae of the agranular reticulum are not covered with ribosomes. Their chemical composition probably varies. For example, the membranes of the pinocytosis vesicles coming from the cell surface probably resemble the plasmalemma, whereas the membranes of vesicles elsewhere in the cell may contain a different array of enzymes and other substances. The juxtanuclear smooth-surfaced vesicles, vacuoles, and cisternae that are gathered around the centrioles of the cell center are called the

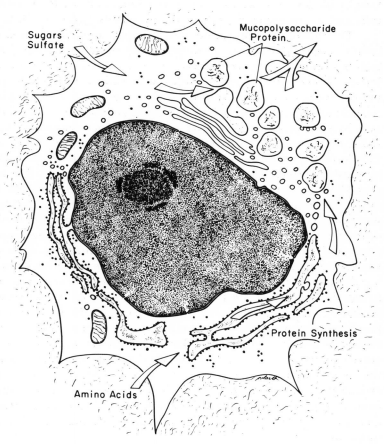

Fig. 4-1. Diagram of the organelles of the cartilage cell. The cell contains abundant granular endoplasmic reticulum (lower part of figure). Here, amino acids are incorporated into protein, presumably on the ribosomes attached to the reticulum. The newly formed proteinaceous product, largely collagen in this case, moves into the vacuoles of the Golgi zone, where it joins the newly synthesized mucopolysaccharide and is secreted from the cell. The mucopolysaccharide (chondroitin sulfate) becomes attached to a noncollagenous protein (chondromucoprotein), a process that might occur in the Golgi zone. The Golgi vacuoles seem to fuse with the cell membrane to exteriorize the mucoproteins and the collagen. The mitochondria of the cartilage cell are thought to provide the energy required for these events. (Drawing prepared in collaboration with J. P. Revel.)

Golgi complex. A specialized agranular reticulum occurs in muscle cells and in the secretory cells of steroid glands (Fawcett, 1966).

The function of the granular endoplasmic reticulum and Golgi complex of protein-secreting epithelial and connective tissue gland cells has been investigated extensively in recent years. Siekevitz and Palade (1960) demonstrated with cytochemical techniques that radioactive leucine is first incorporated in the microsomes (granular reticulum) of pancreatic acinar cells and that protein derived from this compartment becomes part of the zymogen granules. Autoradiographic studies at the electron microscope level by Caro and Palade (1964) and others show that most, if not all, of the newly synthesized proteins pass through the Golgi apparatus. The concept that the ergastoplasm synthesizes proteins destined for the extracellular space, including such permanent proteins as collagen, was extended to connective tissue cells by autoradiographic studies of regenerating cartilage (Revel and Hay, 1963) and healing wounds (Ross and Benditt, see Porter, 1964). The proteins pass from the ergastoplasm into the Golgi complex where mucopolysaccharides are apparently synthesized and added to the product (Peterson and Leblond, 1964; Revel, 1964). The entire process, from incorporation of amino acids and sugars by the cell to the exit of the formed matrix compounds from the cell takes about 2 hours (Fig. 4-1). The ribosomes attached to the granular reticulum are undoubtedly involved in the synthesis of such proteins but the manner in which the proteinaceous product is transposed into the cavity of the reticulum is problematical. The ribosomes occur in long, curled chains which might be called polysomes. The relation of messenger and transfer RNA to the membrane-attached ribonucleoproteins is unknown.

Not all of the ribosomes of the cell are bound to the endoplasmic reticulum. Indeed, in a cell such as a myoblast, which is making proteins that will remain in the cytoplasm, the numerous ribosomes are free for the most part, that is, they are not attached to membranes (Fig. 4-2). The ribosomes may be arranged in groups and chains around the differentiating myofibrils and they seem to synthesize actin and myosin molecules that quickly polymerize into myofilaments (see Hay, 1963; Konigsberg, 1965). A helical arrangement of the ribosomes in developing muscle has been suggested (Waddington, 1963).

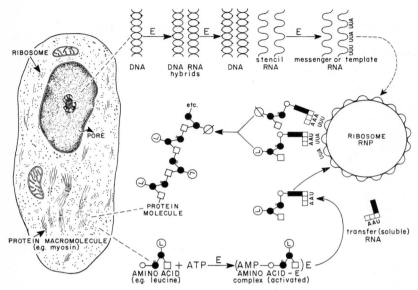

Fig. 4-2. Diagram of a developing muscle cell. Current concepts of messenger RNA synthesis in the nucleus and protein assembly on cytoplasmic ribosomes are presented on the right (see Watson, 1965 for review). We assume that the nucleus of the muscle cell is involved in producing all three of the RNA types depicted on the right (messenger RNA, transfer RNA, and ribosomal RNA). The nucleolus seems particularly implicated in the synthesis of ribosomal RNA. The manner in which these products reach the cytoplasm is still problematical. The most popular speculation is that they pass through pores in the nuclear envelope as indicated here. Amino acids entering the muscle cell are undoubtedly assembled into protein molecules on the cytoplasmic ribosomal units. The protein molecules seem to polymerize very soon thereafter to form definitive myosin and actin filaments. There is no need for the intervention of endoplasmic reticulum and Golgi complex, because the newly formed proteins are destined to remain within the cell. The intracytoplasmic membranes that do occur in muscle cells may be involved in formation of the special conducting organelle of these cells, the smooth-surfaced sarcoplasmic reticulum. Two of the numerous mitochondria of the developing muscle cell are depicted in the drawing on the left.

If we turn now to examine the fine structure of the cytoplasm of a growing cell in a regenerating amphibian limb, we find that the proportion of free ribosomes to membrane-attached ribosomes is high. In blastema cells of the regenerating limb of *Ambystoma* and *Triturus* larvae, the granular reticulum and other membranous organelles are not well developed and the free ribosomes, which seemingly are making proteins to perpetuate the cytoplasm, are abundant (Hay, 1958; Salpeter and Singer, 1962). The cytoplasm is basophilic in its staining reaction for the light microscope and the growing cells are characterized by large, vesicular nuclei and prominent nucleoli. They resemble the mesenchymal cells of the embryonic limb bud. As one might expect, the nuclei are engaged in active nucleic acid and protein synthesis and the chromosomal materials are dispersed to form a loose, euchromatic gel (Hay and Revel, 1963). An autoradiograph viewed in the electron microscope demonstrates dramatically the incorporation of tritiated thymidine into the chromatin of the interphase nucleus during the S phase of the mitotic cycle (Fig. 4-3). The DNA component within the nucleolus also labels at the appropriate time, that is, when the nucleolar-organizing chromosomes replicate. RNA turnover is intensive (Hay, 1965; Bodemer, 1962).

The impression one gains of the growing cell in the regenerating larval limb, and in many regions of the vertebrate embryo as well, is that of an undifferentiated, simplified cell type in which nuclear activities, especially nucleoprotein synthesis, dominate over cytoplasmic activities. One might be tempted to generalize that this is the most suitable morphology for a growing cell completely preoccupied with the progenitor cycle. Indeed, it is easy to slip into the erroneous assumption that this is the only morphology compatible with proliferation and, concomitantly, with pluripotency. At first glance, studies of the fine structure of the so-called totipotent "reserve" cells of hydrozoans and flatworms seem to support this oversimplified assumption.

Fig. 4-3 (*Facing page*) Autoradiograph of a blastema cell viewed in the electron microscope. The regenerating limb of an *Ambystoma* larva was fixed an hour after intraperitoneal administration of tritiated thymidine, as described by Hay and Revel, 1963. A developed silver grain in the autoradiographic emulsion overlying the section looks like a tangled metallic skein at this magnification and resolution. The grains are localized over the diffusely distributed filamentous chromatin of the nucleus (N). Mesenchymal cells of the larval regenerate have abundant cytoplasmic ribosomes, a few mitochondria, some endoplasmic reticulum, and a small Golgi complex. Nucleoli (not shown in this section) are prominent. Interestingly enough, mesenchymal cells are in very close contact with each other at points (arrow). These growing, proliferating cells might be con-

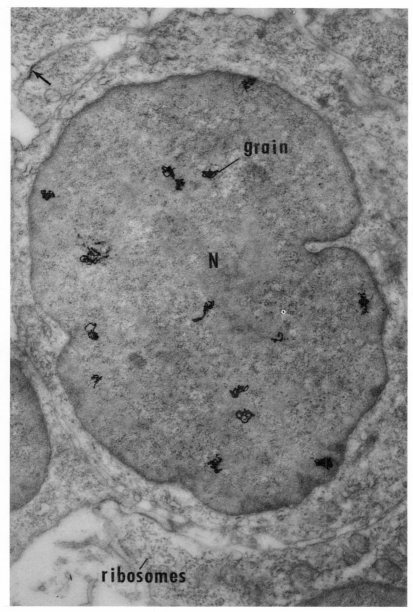

grain

N

ribosomes

sidered as prototypes for our concept of a relatively undifferentiated cell. In comparing this figure with Figs. 4-4 and 4-5, note that the nucleus of the amphibian cell is much larger than the nuclei of cells of other animals. × 12,000.

FINE STRUCTURE OF INTERSTITIAL CELLS AND NEOBLASTS

Slautterback and Fawcett in 1959 described the fine structure of interstitial cells and developing cnidoblasts in several species of *Hydra*. The interstitial cells tend to occur singly or in pairs in the ectoderm (epidermis) near the base of the epithelium (Fig. 4-4). Nuclei are large and vesicular and nucleoli prominent. The basophilia of the cytoplasm as seen with the light microscope proved to be due almost entirely to free ribonucleoprotein granules, rather than to ribosomes associated with endoplasmic reticulum. The interstitial cells possess little or no endoplasmic reticulum. As the cells differentiate into cnidoblasts (cells which will synthesize nematocysts), granular endoplasmic reticulum appears in the cytoplasm. Mitochondria increase in number and the Golgi complex hypertrophies. The nematocyst seems to enlarge by accumulation of proteins derived from the endoplasmic reticulum via the Golgi apparatus. In a sense, then, the nematocyst is the highly organized secretory product of this cell.

The neoblast of the common planarian, *Dugesia tigrina,* seems to be similar to the interstitial cell in its fine structure. It resides within the cellular mesoderm instead of the epidermis and is recognized by its intense cytoplasmic basophilia as viewed in the light microscope. The cells observed in the electron microscope which best correspond to the light microscopists' concept of the neoblast are single cells which contain enormous numbers of free cytoplasmic ribosomes. Mitochondria and membranous cytoplasmic organelles are sparse (Fig. 4-5). Nucleoli are prominent. The nucleus is vesicular and contains clumps of chromatin which are more pronounced after glutaraldehyde fixation (Fig. 4-5) than after osmium fixation (Pederson, 1959).

Thus, it can be concluded that a cell occurs in planarians and in *Hydra* which, even better than the larval blastema cell, exemplifies the morphology of the so-called undifferentiated cell type. The nucleus is engaged in nucleic acid replication, or seemingly is capable of doing so immediately. Nucleolus and free cytoplasmic ribosomes are well developed, one presumably as the result of the activity of the other. No differentiated structures (for example,

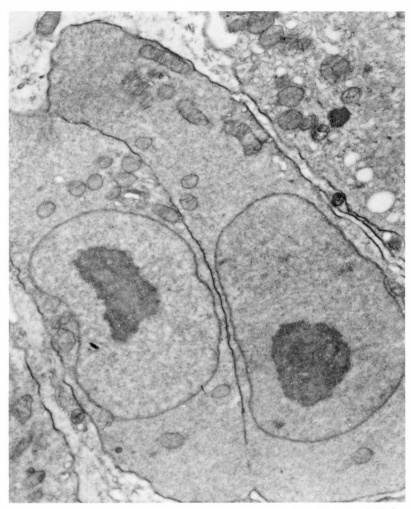

Fig. 4-4. Electron micrograph of two interstitial cells in the epidermis of *Hydra*. Each round, vesicular nucleus has a prominent nucleolus. The dense, granular appearance of the cytoplasm is due to the presence of numerous free ribosomes. Endoplasmic reticulum is virtually absent at this stage. A small Golgi complex appears about the nucleus of the cell on the left and both cells contain a few mitochondria. Later, when the interstitial cells differentiate into cnidoblasts, the membranous organelles become very prominent. The apparent cytoplasmic continuity in the lower half of the figure may be real, for these cells are connected by intercellular bridges and they develop synchronously in small groups. × 11,000. (Courtesy of D. B. Slautterback and D. W. Fawcett, from a micrograph that originally appeared in *J. Biophys. Biochem. Cytol.* 1959, **5**.)

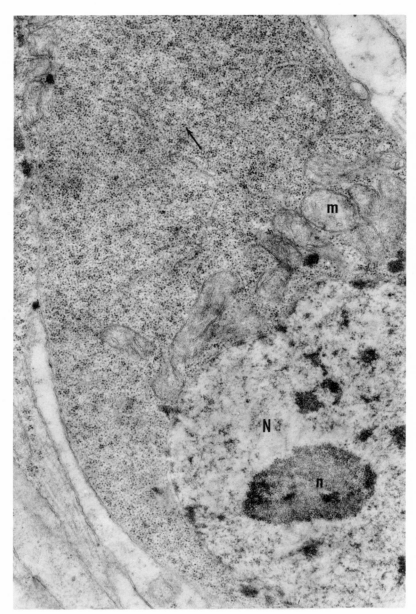

Fig. 4-5. Electron micrograph of a relatively undifferentiated cell in the mesoderm of the flatworm, *Dugesia*. The abundant cytoplasm is full of free ribosomes which

fibrils) are apparent in the cytoplasm or adjoining extracellular space. We will re-examine the meaning of these morphological features in a moment. Let us assume for the sake of the present discussion that this is the morphology one would require of a growing cell that seemingly is pluripotent, such as a neoblast, interstitial cell, or blastema cell.

FINE STRUCTURE OF BLASTEMA CELLS OF ADULT NEWTS

It will come as a surprise, then, to find that the blastema cell of the regenerating limb has a different structure in the adult newt than in the larval salamander (Salpeter and Singer, 1960). The cytoplasm is filled with endoplasmic reticulum and other membranous organelles that characterize a glandular connective tissue cell type. Yet the cells of the adult blastema presumably have the same developmental capacity as those of the larva. If we define cytodifferentiation as the acquisition of specific structural and functional attributes which concentrate the activities of the cell in a particular direction, then we are forced to conclude that the blastema cells of the adult, although they derived from muscle and connective tissues and will reform the limb, are differentiated. This apparent paradox does not mean that the definition of differentiation in terms of morphological criteria is in error. What it means is that we were wrong in attributing developmental capacity only to unspecialized cell types. If we look more closely at the adult limb, it is quite easy to see why the blastema cells resemble fibroblasts. They are surrounded by a collagenous matrix to which they undoubtedly are contributing secretions (Salpeter and Singer, 1960). Yet they synthesize DNA (Fig. 4-6) and divide, and the limb slowly regenerates. While the process never gives rise to a limb in the mammal, nevertheless the ability of fibroblasts to divide cannot be

may be arranged in small clusters (arrow). Endoplasmic reticulum is not prominent. The nucleus (N) is large and vesicular, with a prominent, granular nucleous (n). The washed-out appearance is typical of nuclei fixed in glutaraldehyde followed by osmium tetroxide. A mitochondrion is labeled (m). Cells such as this one would be highly basophilic as viewed in the light microscope after appropriate staining. The cell could, therefore, be classified as a neoblast according to the established nomenclature. × 20,000.

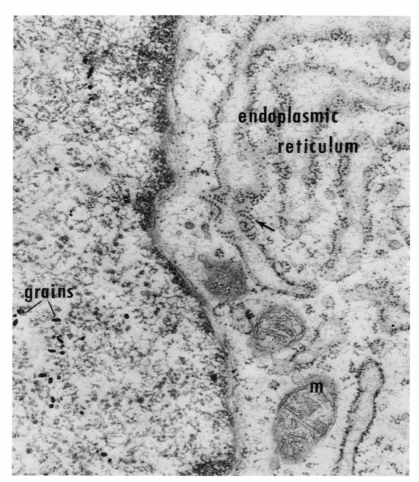

Fig. 4-6. Electron micrograph of part of a blastema cell from the regenerating limb of adult *Triturus*. The endoplasmic reticulum is well developed in these cells. Where the membranes of the cisternae are tangentially cut, the whorled pattern assumed by the attached ribosomes is apparent (arrow). A mitochondrion is labeled (m). Even though these mesenchymatous cells are dividing and presumably have the same developmental potency as the cells of the larval regenerate (Figure 4-3), they are more differentiated in the sense that the endoplasmic reticulum is as abundant as in secretory cell types (such as fibroblasts). The preparation illustrated is an autoradiograph and the tissue was treated with tritiated thymidine. The silver grains over the nucleus on the left appear as small dots rather than tiny skeins because only a short exposure to a fine-grained developer was employed in the processing of the autoradiograph. The initial grain

denied (Chapter Three). Other secretory cells, such as chondrocytes, thyroid parenchymal cells, and pancreatic acinar cells divide occasionally and they do this without losing the ergastoplasm and membranous organelles that characterize their "state of differentiation." Indeed, the mesenchymal cells of the embryo have abundant granular endoplasmic reticulum if they are making collagen (Hay, 1962). The evidence thus far forces us to conclude that: (a) the so-called pluripotentiality of blastema cells is not directly dependent on the morphological state of differentiation; (b) the morphological configuration and function of the connective tissue gland cell (fibroblast) is not, in itself, incompatible with cell division.

RE-EVALUATION OF THE MORPHOLOGY OF RESERVE CELLS

It is quite clear that it is the undifferentiated appearance of the interstitial cell and neoblast which led investigators to think the cells played a role in regeneration. The striking basophilic cytoplasm and prominent nucleolus are reminiscent of growing embryonic cells and so we reason that these are "totipotent reserve cells." This is the kind of thinking that has gotten the morphologist into trouble with the embryologist in the past. *Yet the fault lies with the experimental embryologist, with the embryological concept that cell differentiation is the same thing as limitation of developmental potency.* We will examine the evidence for this concept in a moment. But first, let us re-examine the experimental evidence for a role of reserve cells in regeneration.

In Chapter One, radiation experiments were described in which the effect of the treatment was thought to be on the planarian neoblast. Basophilic cells were said to migrate into an irradiated area to repopulate the tissue which now becomes capable of regeneration. The possibility that the migrating cells revived the old irradiated tissues, or that they derived from differentiated unirradiated tissues, was not ruled out. A similar line of reasoning was

size was also quite small (Kodak NTE emulsion). The autoradiograph leaves no doubt that cells with abundant endoplasmic reticulum can synthesize DNA. (Courtesy of M. M. Salpeter and L. Bachmann, from a micrograph that originally appeared in *J. Cell Biol.*, 1964, **22**: 476.)

applied in the case of *Hydra* subjected to irradiation. While the possibility that interstitial cells play a role in budding in some forms cannot be ruled out, it will be recalled that interstitial cells are not present in budding zones in all species. Recently, Haynes and Burnett (Chapter One) demonstrated that *Hydra viridis* can regenerate from an endodermal fragment completely lacking in interstitial cells. The cytology of the transformation has now been studied in detail. A blastema of morphologically undifferentiated cells has not been observed to form. The endodermal cells may transform first into interstitial cells or they may transform directly into the formed ectodermal types which they recreate.

Thinking that the bud or blastema which forms on the cut surface of a planarian fragment might at least be composed of undifferentiated cells, we have recently examined sections of regenerating planarians in the electron microscope. The baffling array of morphological specializations that we discovered in the regenerate awaits more detailed analysis. However, a blastema composed of simple neoblasts was not observed. Many of the basophilic cells had abundant endoplasmic reticulum (Fig. 4-7) and the whole tissue had the appearance of an epithelial rather than a mesenchymal mass.

It is quite possible that the only normal function of the interstitial cell of *Hydra* is to replace cnidoblasts as they are lost on the "battle front." These cells could be said to be specialized for rapid cell division and subsequent metaplasia into cnidoblasts. In the planarian, the epidermis contains special slime-secreting cells whose base extends through the basement membrane into the inner epithelial mass termed the mesoderm. It is conceivable that the so-called neoblast is normally merely a replacement cell for this dispensable gland cell. The neoblasts described in annelids have

Fig. 4-7 (*Facing page*). Electron micrograph of a mesodermal cell in the anterior end of a regenerating flatworm (*Dugesia tigrina*) 4 days after cutting the worm in two. This cell would be basophilic as viewed in the light microscope because of the abundant ergastoplasm (arrows). It would probably be classified as a neoblast, therefore, but the numerous granular cisternae and granular inclusions indicate that it must be a differentiated secretory cell of some kind. The population of basophilic cells in the regenerating planarian is seemingly a mixed one, then. Some cells are relatively undifferentiated (Fig. 4-5), while others have the fibroblast or gland-cell morphology illustrated here. N, nucleus; m, mitochondria. Fixation, glutaraldehyde followed by osmium. × 20,000.

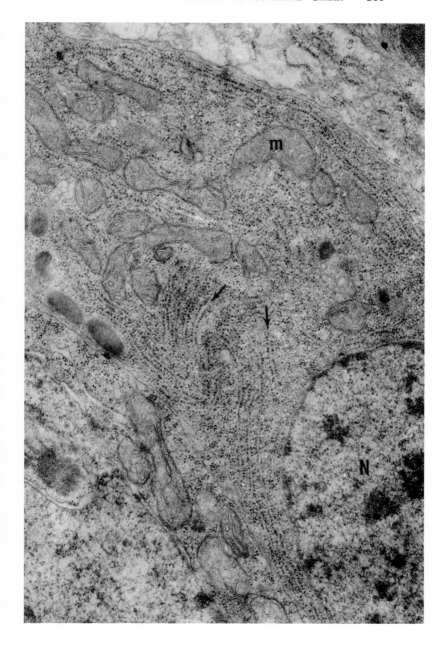

varying locations in the body, but are never numerous. Do they, in fact, have some equally specialized function in the adult worm? We cannot, of course, answer these questions at the moment. Certainly, a reinvestigation of the reality of the "totipotent" invertebrate reserve cell and its so-called role in regeneration is in order. The problem might be solved by use of the combined morphological and physiological techniques that are available today.

The electron microscopic studies that have been done with hydrozoans and planarians, therefore, as well as those with amphibians, call our attention to the possibility that the simplification of cell structure noted under certain conditions is not an expression of a pluripotential or totipotential state, but is instead a specialized morphology which is related to quick replacement of dispensable cells in the invertebrate and rapid growth of the limb in the larval amphibian. In viewing these phenomena as a whole, one is tempted to agree with Swann (1958) that the so-called undifferentiated state often exhibited by actively growing cells should, in fact, be regarded as a state of differentiation, a specialized condition for synthesis and turnover of those proteins, nucleic acids, and formed structures necessary for proliferation. To go one step further, we could say that simplification of structure is the somatic cell specialization for proliferation. A cell which is forced to carry its own nutritive supply and to divide even more rapidly than the somatic cells, is a highly differentiated cell by any standards (other than developmental potency). The frog oöcyte for example, contains an ordered array of protein-storing structures that defies simple description. It stores ribosomes and other nucleoproteins and their precursors (Brown, 1965). The nucleoli are dispensed with; so rapid is the cell division that they would hardly have time to reform (Chapter Three). The archaeocyte of the sponge gemmule is another example of a totipotent cell which is highly specialized in its morphology (Ruthman, 1965). The cytoplasmic differentiation which it exhibits is undoubtedly of value to its survival and, ultimately, to its ability to recreate a sponge.

THE QUESTION OF DEVELOPMENTAL POTENCY

How much more simple the situation would be for the histologist untutored in experimental embryology if cellular differentiation could be defined as the attainment of a specific functional capacity, with the morphological expression attendant upon this capacity, without being continuously concerned with the potencies or possibilities latent in a cell which may or may not be realized at some future time under different environmental conditions!

If we were to accept this opinion, expressed by A. B. Dawson (1940, p. 92) then all differentiation would, of course, have to be defined with reference to some specified point. Thus, we might speak of the growing, mesenchymal cell type as "relatively undifferentiated" compared to the fully formed muscle fiber. We would do this, however, without casting any aspersions about the developmental potency of the cells. There is no such thing as an "undifferentiated state," according to this theory. The ovum might be thought of as a cell specialized for the initiation of development. At gastrulation, the cells pass from one state of differentiation to another. Such morphological characterizations conflict with the embryological concept of differentiation for the following reason. Because of the results of experiments on amphibian eggs in the first part of this century, the embryologist has taken the view that cell differentiation is by definition a progressive series of irreversible restrictions in developmental potency. Let us briefly examine some of the evidence for this conflicting viewpoint.

The idea that cell differentiation in the vertebrate is progressive and irreversible stems from experiments in which parts of the blastula or early gastrula were transplanted to other embryos. Such young pieces of tissue almost invariably develop in accord with their new surroundings; for example, a piece of presumptive eye tissue might become somite if moved to the back of an older embryo. If it does change its fate, then the original piece of tissue is said to have been "undifferentiated" or "undetermined." The parts or tissues seem to become "determined" during gastrulation. Henceforth, they "self-differentiate" into the cell types that the transplanted region would have formed anyway, if left undisturbed in the donor embryo. It often is said that the developmental capacity of a cell is a better index of its state of differentiation than any of the "overt" morphological or physiological criteria of differentiation (see Grobstein, 1959). This statement assumes, and this is the crux of the problem, that developmental capacity and cytodifferentiation are inversely related. Neither the developmental capacity nor the developmental potential (if one wishes to distinguish between the two terms) of a single cell can be easily measured, as Dawson so clearly recognized. The experiments that gave rise to the concept of determination were applicable only to tissues (parts) of the embryo. That the concept should have been applied to cytodifferentiation was not the intention of the original investigators (see Spemann, 1938, p. 211). No experiment has been devised which actually tests the developmental capacity of a single cell. Even recent work on single muscle cells in culture is a measure of the effect of a conditioned culture medium on the cells (Konigsberg and Hauschka, 1965).

Recently, however, it has become possible to transplant nuclei from somatic cells to enucleated eggs (Briggs and King, 1959). While it has not been proved that all somatic cell nuclei have developmental capacity, it has been shown that nuclei from differentiated intestinal cells can support development of the amphibian egg (Gurdon, 1962). Such somatic nuclei, which contain nucleoli, lose these nuclear organelles, enlarge, and assume the morphology of the enormous nuclei that characterize the blastomere (Gurdon and Brown, 1965). If the double standard definition of differentiation alluded to above is applied to these experiments, then one is forced to conclude that the differentiated intestinal nucleus was undifferentiated. It would be far better to remove the latter connotation from the definition.

It is, of course, the cytoplasm of the ovum which brings about the changes observed in the somatic nuclear transplants (Gurdon and Brown, 1965). Yet in this case, the differentiation of the cytoplasm is, if you will, designed to be reversible. Contained within its cortex or inner organelles is all of the information that is needed to bring the cleaving ovum to gastrulation (see Briggs and King, 1959). Examples of the reversibility of the cytoplasmic differentiation of somatic cells can also be found, however. Consider only the transformation of the pigmented retinal epithelium of the newt into lens cells, on the one hand, and neural sensory cells, on the other (Chapter Two); the transformation of dedifferentiating muscle cells into fibroblastlike blastema cells in the regenerating limb of the adult newt; and the changes that must occur in the endodermal cells of *Hydra* before they transform into ectodermal cells. What is truly remarkable is that such cells as these, which can grow and faithfully reproduce a missing part, are under normal conditions so stable, so content with one or another specialized niche. Except in cases where the nuclear material is eliminated partly (as in certain insect cells) or completely (as in mammalian red blood cells), cytodifferentiation does not, by definition, have to be irreversible. It would probably be best, then, to follow Dawson's advice in this matter; to stop trying to define cytodifferentiation in terms of developmental capacity; to come to terms with morphological, biochemical, and physiological manifestations in our efforts to devise a workable definition of cell differentiation. These easily observed characteristics of differentiated cells—morphological, biochemical, and physiological specializations—may have a great deal to do with the developmental capacity of the cell (in the case of the gametes); they may reflect temporary but necessary cell activities which contribute to the structure of the organ as a whole without impeding its development (as in the regenerating adult *Triturus* limb); or they may in themselves interfere with cell proliferation, and consequently with organ recapitulation, and therefore be disposed of during regeneration. In the next section we will attempt to explore the meaning of dedifferentiation from this cytological point of view, stressing the relation of the process to cell proliferation and tissue reorganization, without casting aspersions on the developmental capacities of more differentiated cells.

THE SIGNIFICANCE OF DEDIFFERENTIATION

In the sense that the inner cells of the amputated salamander limb do revert to a mesenchymal cell type during the formation of a blastema, it can be said that dedifferentiation does occur in amphibian regeneration (Fig. 4-8). The term connotes in this case two simultaneous phenomena: (1) loss of structures associated with the differentiated state (not in Swann's sense of the term, but meaning those formed elements, such as myofibrils, which characterize a specialized somatic cell in the usual sense); (2) acquisition of the nuclear and cytoplasmic morphology and physiology compatible with cell division. According to this definition, if (1) occurs without (2), the process is not dedifferentiation. It is degeneration, or some other phenomenon. In the amphibian limb, we do not know the exact fate of the dedifferentiated mesenchymal cells, any more

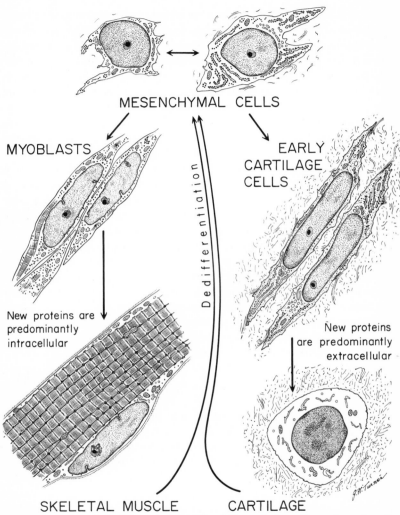

Fig. 4-8. Diagram of dedifferentiation and redifferentiation of muscle and cartilage cells during limb regeneration in the amphibian. During differentiation the mesenchymal cells that become myoblasts accumulate cytoplasmic ribosomes which play a role in the synthesis of muscle proteins. When myoblasts fuse to form skeletal muscle fibers, all DNA synthesis stops. The fibers must break up and transform into more simplified mononucleated cells, if the component cells are to proliferate. The differentiating chondrocyte, on the other hand, is characterized by abundant granular reticulum and a large Golgi complex during the

than we know the exact fate of each mesenchymal cell in the embryonic limb bud. We do know that cells derived from muscle and connective tissue proper somehow create a skeleton in regenerating limbs after exarticulation (Thornton, 1938). It is tempting to think that the blastema cells are pleuripotent. Yet, dedifferentiation also occurs in individual muscles after injury and here the cells merely redifferentiate into muscle. Dedifferentiation can occur in growing tissue cultures without any accompanying redifferentiation (see Holtzer, 1963). It is only in rare instances, however, that metaplasia, or modulation if you prefer, occurs in vertebrates without a phase of dedifferentiation and proliferation and these are instances of transformation to a phagocytic state (Weiss, 1950).

Some authors have taken the view that cell dedifferentiation, and especially the concomitant proliferation, is an integral part of metaplasia in regeneration. In studies of Wolffian lens regeneration (Chapter Two), Takata *et al.* suggest that during the phase of dedifferentiation, the old pattern of genetic transcription in the dorsal iris cells is interrupted. RNA synthesis begins to increase shortly after the injury. Then DNA synthesis ensues and cells divide a number of times before differentiating into lens fibers. The replication of genetic material seemed to precede the transcription of new genetic information. Attractive as the idea is, it would be difficult to say which is cause and which is effect in such a system. If the new lens rudiment, or the limb for that matter, is going to increase in size then the cells must proliferate; to do this they require increased RNA synthesis and renewed DNA synthesis.

period when it is secreting a cartilaginous matrix. It is still capable of dividing at this time. The quiescent cartilage cell (bottom right) must be released from the cartilaginous matrix by a process of dedifferentiation in order to become metabolically active again. Blastema cells vary in the amount of endoplasmic reticulum they contain, being more fibroblastlike (top right) in the limb regenerate of an adult salamander than a larval salamander (top left). In all documented cases of regeneration in vertebrates, formed cell types rather than "reserve cells" are used for regeneration. Herein lies the significance of dedifferentiation. Differentiated products are not retained if the cells begin to proliferate very actively. The degree to which the cell form and organelles are altered seems to depend on the nature of the remodeling job that will ensue. (From E. D. Hay, "Cytological studies of dedifferentiation and differentiation in regenerating amphibian limbs" in *Regeneration,* edited by Dorothea Rudnick, Copyright © 1962, The Ronald Press Company.)

It would be interesting to know whether or not some proliferation is necessary for regeneration in the invertebrates. Seemingly, it is not, although cell division must eventually occur if the regenerate is to approach the size of the original animal. In *Tubularia,* cells in both epithelial layers seem to flow toward the cut end. Do they dedifferentiate? Do they proliferate? Do they redifferentiate tissue for tissue? What are the cytological events that actually occur in planaria and *Hydra* during regeneration? As we have seen, the role of "reserve cells" is enigmatic. Do the differentiated cell types in these organisms transform into other cell types during regeneration? And if they transform can they do this without significant dedifferentiation?[1]

Speculations about the significance of proliferation in embryonic metaplasia also can be found in the literature. In the chick embryo, localized proliferation is observed in the dermis at the time of feather induction and this is followed by an increase in mitosis in the epidermis which now produces new specific proteins (Ben-Or and Bell, 1965). There is no DNA synthesis in the epithelial cap before feather outgrowth (Wessells, 1965). There are certainly many other cases where proliferation seems to precede differentiation of the cells involved. However, we should recall that the differ-

[1] This question has now been partially answered by L. E. Davis, A. L. Burnett, J. F. Haynes, and V. R. Munaw, 1966, "A histological and ultrastructural study of dedifferentiation and redifferentiation of digestive and gland cells in *Hydra viridis," Develop. Biol.,* in press. Isolated gastrodermis from the green *Hydra* was grown in culture as described in Chapter One (Haynes and Burnett, 1963). The events that occur in the transformation of (1) absorptive digestive cells to epidermal (epitheliomuscular) cells and (2) glandular intestinal cells to cnidoblasts, were observed in the electron microscope. In the first case, the digestive cells located on the exterior of the explant transformed directly into epidermal cells, acquiring musclelike organelles in the process and losing the symbiont algae and other characteristics of the typical digestive cell. In the second case, gland cells on the exterior of the explant reverted to undifferentiated-appearing interstitial cells, losing granular reticulum and other organelles along the way, and then seemingly they passed through a stage of proliferation before differentiating into typical cnidoblasts with abundant granular reticulum and Golgi membranes. These provocative results seem to provide in the one case, a fairly clear-cut example of cellular metaplasia in an invertebrate without an intermediate "undifferentiated" or proliferative phase. In the second case (gland cell to cnidoblast), cell dedifferentiation as defined here (loss of specialized products accompanied by proliferation) is an integral part of the transformation. It will be important to prove, by autoradiographic studies, that the digestive cells transforming into epidermal cells do not synthesize DNA, because of the implications for metaplastic mechanisms discussed in the text.

entiated state (defined in Dawson's sense) is sometimes incompatible with cell division. Thus, if the part needs to increase in size to achieve its definitive form, it had best do most of its growing before the cells become committed to a course of specialized protein synthesis.

In the last measure, none of these generalizations holds up exactly, in terms of the over-all spectrum of cell activity. In Chapter Three, we saw that renewing cell populations, the surface epithelia, and hematopoietic tissues maintain a partially differentiated progenitor pool of cells that proliferate. One group of stable cells, the glandular epithelial and connective tissue cells, can divide without dedifferentiation (pancreatic acinar cells, liver cells, fibroblasts, chondroblasts). A striking case in point is the highly differentiated Leydig (mucous) cell of amphibian epidermis. The cytoplasm is full of specialized granules and organelles, but the nucleus may be actively synthesizing DNA or dividing at any time. The genetic material itself need not be transcribing and replicating at the same time to support such processes. Indeed, the cause of the apparent antagonism between mitosis and "differentiation" may have nothing to do with the cells' accumulation of specialized products. The most dramatic dedifferentiation is observed in striated muscle cells preparing for proliferation, but the reason may be only that the syncytial state itself is incompatible with cell division.

Perhaps the greatest conceptual fallacy of all would be to look at the dedifferentiation which occurs in certain regenerating systems as a method by which the cells regain the developmental capacities of the "undifferentiated totipotent cell." Even if there were reason to think that the nuclei had lost developmental potency, which there is not, who or what is the newly created "totipotent cell"? In vertebrates, it is the cytoplasmic differentiation of the zygote which seems to bring about any expression of "totipotency." The blastema cells would have to be grown in a nonexistent zoological equivalent of coconut milk (Steward, 1963) to reproduce an embryo. The problem of the cells in a regenerating limb is not to regain the presumably lost potentials of the blastomeres, but rather, to reproduce a limb, to grow rapidly enough in a controlled system to provide enough cells for the morphogenetic pattern to be reinstated. It is this dramatic reinstatement of a complex tissue pattern that distinguishes limb regeneration from the kind of compensatory hypertrophy that occurs in, say, liver regeneration. Herein probably lies the significance of the blastema. Its mass or size, as we have seen in Chapter Two, may be one of the critical factors in determining the success of limb redifferentiation. A blastema can be created quickly by relatively undifferentiated mesenchymal cells or slowly by fibroblastlike cells derived from the formed tissues through dedifferentiation; the developmental capacity of the cells is seemingly the same in both cases, even though the fibroblastlike cells of the adult *Triturus* limb by definition are more differentiated than the simplified blastema cells of the larval limb (Hay, 1958; Salpeter and Singer, 1960).

Harrison (1933) has warned us to beware of the "anthropomorphisms and relics of our demonology . . . which may not only lend a false sense of security to our explanations but also may suggest foolish questions that never can be answered." It is almost impossible, unfortunately, to avoid thinking of the regeneration cell in terms of the enigmatic significance of "totipotency." We would be far better off, however, if we turned to the zygote itself to study this particular reproductive principle in the vertebrate. The significance of dedifferentiation is to be found in the fact that formed cell types are used for the process of regeneration. To reform a limb, lens, or other complex part, the cells must reorganize their structure and they must proliferate. What we really want to know is how and why cells regenerate a limb in one case, form a bud that produces a new animal in another, and fail to grow at all in another. Genetic control mechanisms of a sort not yet visualized in our approaches to the problem may be involved in the evolution of the differing patterns of regeneration in the various animals. Nature seemingly has not found it necessary or economical to set aside "undifferentiated reserve cells" for most regenerative processes, even though we think she should have. Let us try to discover what she has done, what kind of control mechanisms she has evolved to create the diversity and order of living cells and to insure the reproduction and consequent immortality of her product.

▶ References

Chapter One
Invertebrates

ANDERSON, J. M., 1965. "Studies on visceral regeneration in sea-stars. II. Regeneration of pyloric caeca in *Asteriidae*, with notes on the source of cells in regenerating organs," *Biol. Bull.*, **128**: 1–23.

BALAMUTH, W., 1940. "Regeneration in protozoa; a problem of morphogenesis," *Quart. Rev. Biol.*, **15**: 290–337.

BALINSKY, B. I., 1965. *An introduction to embryology.* Philadelphia: W. B. Saunders Co.

BARTH, L. G., 1940. "The process of regeneration in hydroids," *Biol. Rev.*, **15**: 405–420.

———, 1955. "Regeneration: Invertebrates." In *Analysis of development*, ed. by B. H. Willier, P. A. Weiss, and V. Hamburger. Philadelphia: W. B. Saunders Co., pp. 664–673.

BERRILL, N. J., 1961. *Growth, development, and pattern.* San Francisco: W. H. Freeman and Co.

BIBERHOFER, R., 1906. "Über Regeneration bei *Amphioxus lanceolatus*," *Arch. Entwicklungsmech. Or.*, **22**: 15–17.

BLISS, D. E., 1959. "Factors controlling regeneration of legs and molting in land crabs." In *Physiology of insect development*, ed. by F. L. Campbell. Chicago: University of Chicago Press, pp. 131–140.

BODENSTEIN, D. 1955. "Contributions to the problem of regeneration in insects," *J. Exp. Zool.*, **129**: 209–224.

———, 1957. "Studies on nerve regeneration in Periplaneta americana," *J. Exp. Zool.*, **136**: 89–116.

BOUILLON, J., 1955. "Le bourgeonnement manubrial de la méduse *Limnocnida tanganyicae*," *Acad. Roy. Sci. Coloniales (Brussels), Classe Sci. Tech. Mem., Collection in 8*, **1**: 1152–1180.

BRØNSTEDT, H. V., 1955. "Planarian regeneration," *Biol. Rev.*, **30**: 65–126.

BURNETT, A. L., 1962. "The maintenance of form in *Hydra*." In *Regeneration*, ed. by D. Rudnick. New York: The Ronald Press Co., pp. 27–52.

CHANDEBOIS, R., 1965. "Cell transformation systems in Planarians." In *Regeneration in animals and related problems*, ed. by V. Kiortsis and H. A. L. Tranpusch. Amsterdam, Netherlands: North-Holland Publishing Co., pp. 131–142.

CHILD, C. M., 1941. *Patterns and problems of development.* Chicago: University of Chicago Press.

119

CHILD, F. M., 1965. "Mechanisms controlling the regeneration of cilia in Tetrahymena," *J. Cell Biol.*, 27: 18A.

CLARK, M. E., 1965. "Cellular aspects of regeneration in the Polychaete *Nephtys.*" In *Regeneration in animals and related problems,* ed. by V. Kiortsis and H. A. L. Trampusch. Amsterdam, Netherlands: North-Holland Publishing Co., pp. 240–249.

COWDEN, R., and D. BODENSTEIN, 1961. "A cytochemical investigation of striated muscle differentiation in regenerating limbs of the roach, *Periplanata americana,*" *Embryologia (Nagoya),* 6: 36–50.

DIEHL, F. A., and A. L. BURNETT, 1965. "The role of interstitial cells in the maintenance of hydra. III. Regeneration of hypostome and tentacles," *J. Exp. Zool.,* 158: 299–318.

DURAND, J. B., 1960. "Limb regeneration and endocrine activity in the crayfish," *Biol. Bull.,* 118: 250–261.

FLICKINGER, R. A., and S. J. COWARD, 1962. "The induction of cephalic differentiation in regenerating *Dugesia* dorotocephala in the presence of the normal head and in unwounded tails," *Develop. Biol.,* 5: 179–204.

FREEMAN, G., 1964. "The role of blood cells in the process of asexual reproduction in the tunicate, *Perophora viridis,*" *J. Exp. Zool.,* 156: 157–183.

FULTON, C., 1959. "Re-examination of an inhibitor of regeneration in *Tubularia,*" *Biol. Bull.,* 116: 232–238.

GATES, G. E., 1951. "Regeneration in an Indian earthworm, *Perionyx millardi* Stephenson." *Proc. Indian Acad. Sci.,* 34: 115–147.

HAMBURGER, V., 1965. "Regeneration," *Encyclopedia Britannica,* Vol. 19. Chicago: W. Benton.

HAYNES, J., and A. L. BURNETT, 1963. "Dedifferentiation and redifferentiation of cells in *Hydra viridis,*" *Science,* 142: 1481–1483.

HERLANT-MEEWIS, H., 1964. "Regeneration in annelids." In *Advances in morphogenesis,* Vol. 4, ed. by M. Abercrombie and J. Brachet. New York: Academic Press, Inc., pp. 155–215.

HUMPHREYS, T., 1963. Chemical dissolution and *in vitro* reconstruction of sponge cell adhesions. I. Isolation and functional demonstration of the components involved," *Develop. Biol.,* 8: 27–47.

HUXLEY, J., 1911. "Regeneration of Sycon," *Phil. Trans. Roy. Soc. London, Ser. B,* 202: 165–190.

———, 1921. "Studies in dedifferentiation. II. Dedifferentiation and resorption in *Perophora,*" *Quart. J. Microscop. Sci.,* 65: 643–698.

———, 1925. "Studies in dedifferentiation. VI. Reduction phenomena in *Clavellina lepadiformis,*" *Pubblilagioni della Stazione Zoologiea di Napoli,* 7: 1–35.

HYMAN, L. H., 1940. "Aspects of regeneration in annelids," *Am. Naturalist,* 83: 139–152.

———, 1955. *The invertebrates, Vol. 4, Echinodermata.* New York: McGraw-Hill Book Co., Inc.

KRISHNAKUMARAN, A., and H. A. SCHNEIDERMAN, 1964. "Developmental capacities of the cells of an adult moth," *J. Exp. Zool.*, **157**: 293–306.

LANGE, M. M., 1920. "On the regeneration and finer structure of the arms of the cephalopods," *J. Exp. Zool.*, **31**: 1–57.

LENDER, T., 1962. "Factors in morphogenesis of regenerating fresh-water planaria." In *Advances in morphogenesis,* Vol. 2, ed. by M. Abercrombie and J. Brachet. New York: Academic Press, Inc., pp. 305–331.

LENHOFF, H., and W. F. LOOMIS, 1961. *The biology of Hydra.* Miami, Fla.: University of Miami Press.

LUND, E. J., 1917. "Reversibility of morphogenetic processes in *Bursaria,*" *J. Exp. Zool.*, **24**: 1–34.

———, 1947. *Biolectric fields and growth.* Austin, Tex.: University of Texas Press.

MOMENT, G. B., 1946. "A study of growth limitation in earthworms," *J. Exp. Zool.*, **103**: 487–506.

———, 1951. "Simultaneous anterior and posterior regeneration and other growth phenomena in Maldanid polychaetes," *J. Exp. Zool.*, **117**: 1–14.

———, 1953. "A theory of growth limitation," *Am. Naturalist*, **87**: 139–153.

MORGAN, T. H., 1901. *Regeneration.* New York: The Macmillan Company.

———, 1904. "Germ layers and regeneration," *Arch. Entwicklungsmech. Or.*, **18**: 261–264.

NEEDHAM, A. E., 1952. *Regeneration and wound-healing.* New York: John Wiley & Sons, Inc.

———, 1965. "Regeneration in the Arthropod and its endocrine control." In *Regeneration in animals and related problems,* ed. by V. Kiortsis and H. A. L. Trampusch. Amsterdam, Netherlands: North-Holland Publishing Co., pp. 283–323.

OKADA, Y. K., 1929. "Regeneration and fragmentation in the syllidian polychaetes," *Arch. Entwicklungsmech. Or.*, **115**: 542–600.

PENZLIN, H., 1964. "The significance of the nervous system for regeneration in insects," *Arch. Entwicklungsmech. Or.*, **155**: 152–161.

RASMONT, R., 1962. "The physiology of gemmulation in fresh-water sponges." In *Regeneration,* ed. by D. Rudnick. New York: The Ronald Press Co., pp. 3–26.

ROSE, S. M., 1957. "Cellular interaction during differentiation," *Biol. Rev.*, **32**: 351–382.

———, 1963. "Polarized control of regional structure in *Tubularia,*" *Develop. Biol.*, **7**: 488–501.

———, and F. C. ROSE, 1941. "The role of a cut surface in *Tubularia* regeneration," *Physiol. Zool.*, **14**: 328–343.

Schotté, O. E., 1940. "The origin and morphogenetic potencies of regenerates." *Growth Suppl.*, 59–76.

Scott, F. M., and J. E. Schuh, 1963. "Intraspecific reaggregation in *Amaroecium constellatum* labeled with tritiated thymidine," *Acta Embryol. Morphol. Exptl.*, **6**: 39–54.

Smith, S. D., 1963. "Specific inhibition of regeneration in *Clymella torquata*," *Biol. Bull.*, **125**: 542–555.

Steinberg, M. S., 1954. "Studies on the mechanism of physiological dominance in *Tubularia*," *J. Exp. Zool.*, **127**: 1–26.

———, 1955. "Cell movement, rate of regeneration, and the axial gradient in *Tubularia. Biol. Bull.*, **108**: 219–234.

Steinberg, S. N., 1963. "The regeneration of whole polyps from ectodermal fragments of scyphistoma larvae of *Aurelia aurita*," *Biol. Bull.*, **124**: 337–343.

Stephan-Dubois, F., 1965. "Les neoblastes dans la regeneration chez les Planaires." In *Regeneration in animals and related problems*, ed. by V. Kiortsis and H. A. L. Trampusch. Amsterdam, Netherlands: North-Holland Publishing Co., pp. 112–130.

Stinson, B. D., 1964. "The response of x-irradiated limbs of adult urodeles to normal tissue grafts. IV. Comparative effects of autografts and homografts of complete forearm regenerates," *J. Exp. Zool.*, **157**: 159–177.

Stolte, H. A., 1936. "Die Herkernft des Zellmaterials bei regenerativen Vorgangen der wirbellosen Tiere," *Biol. Rev.*, **11**: 1–48.

Stone, R. G., 1933. "Radium irradiation effects on regeneration in *Euratella chamberlin*," *Carnegie Inst. Wash. Publ.*, **435**: 157–166.

Tardent, P., 1963. "Regeneration in the Hydrozoa," *Biol. Rev.*, **38**: 293–333.

Tartar, V., 1961. *The biology of Stentor.* New York: Pergamon Press, Inc.

Thouveny, Y., 1965. "Histological aspects of regeneration in *Polydora flava:* evidence from irradiation and synthetic culture medium." In *Regeneration in animals and related problems*, ed. by V. Kiortsis and H. A. L. Trampusch. Amsterdam, Netherlands: North-Holland Publishing Co., pp. 262–271.

Tucker, M., 1959. "Inhibitory control of regeneration in nemertean worms," *J. Morphol.*, **105**: 569–600.

Tweedell, K. S., 1961. "Regeneration of the enteropneust, *Saccoglossus kowalevskii*," *Biol. Bull.*, **120**: 118–127.

Vorontsova, M. A., and L. D. Liosner, 1960. *Asexual propagation and regeneration.* New York: Pergamon Press, Inc.

Weisz, P. B., 1954. "Morphogenesis in protozoa," *Quart. Rev. Biol.*, **29**: 207–229.

———, 1955. "Chemical inhibition of regeneration in *Stentor coerulens*," *J. Cellular Comp. Physiol.*, **46**: 517–527.

Wigglesworth, V. B., 1964. "The hormonal regulation of growth and reproduction in insects," *Advan. Insect Physiol.*, **3**: 247–336.

Williams, N. E., 1964. "Structural development in synchronously dividing *Tetrahymena pyriformis*." In *Synchrony in cell division and growth*, ed. by E. Zeuthen. New York: Interscience Publishers, Inc., pp. 159–175.

WILSON, H. V., 1907. "On some phenomena of coalescence and regeneration in sponges," *J. Exp. Zool.,* **5**: 245–258.

WOLFF, E., 1962. "Recent researches on the regeneration of planaria." In *Regeneration,* ed. by D. Rudnick. New York: The Ronald Press Co., pp. 53–84.

WOLSKY, A., 1957. "Compensatory hyper-regeneration in the antennae of Hemiptera," *Nature,* **180**: 1144–1145.

WOODRUFF, L. S., and A. L. BURNETT, 1965. "The origin of the blastemal cells in *Dugesia tigrina,*" *Exp. Cell Res.,* **38**: 295–305.

ZHINKIN, L., 1936. "The influence of the nervous system on regeneration in *Rhynchelmis limosella Hof., J. Exp. Zool.,* **73**: 43–65.

ZWILLING, E., 1963. "Formation of endoderm from ectoderm in *Cordylophora,*" *Biol. Bull.,* **124**: 368–378.

Chapter Two
Amphibians and Lower Vertebrates

ANTON, H. J., 1961. "Zur Frage der Aktivierung der gewebe im Extremitätenstumpf bei Urodelin vor der Blastembildung," *Arch. Entwicklungsmech. Or.,* **153**: 363–369.

————, 1965. "The origin of blastema cells and protein synthesis during forelimb regeneration in *Triturus.*" In *Regeneration in animals and related problems,* ed. by V. Kiortsis and H. A. L. Trampusch. Amsterdam, Netherlands: North-Holland Publishing Co., pp. 377–395.

BARBER, L. W., 1944. "Correlations between wound healing and regeneration in forelimbs and tails of lizards," *Anat. Record,* **89**: 441–453.

BECKER, R. O., 1961. "The bioelectric factors in amphibian-limb regeneration," *J. Bone Joint Surg.,* **43-A**: 643–656.

BIEBER, S., and G. H. HITCHINGS, 1959. "Effects of growth-inhibitors on amphibian tail blastema," *Cancer Res.,* **19**: 112–115.

BODEMER, C. W., 1958. "The development of nerve-induced supernumerary limbs in the adult newt, *Triturus viridescens,*" *J. Morphol.,* **102**: 555–582.

————, 1964. "Evocation of regrowth phenomena in anuran limbs by electrical stimulation of the nerve supply," *Anat. Rec.,* **148**: 441–448.

BRETSCHER, A., and P. TSCHUMI, 1951. "Gestufte reduktion von chemisch behandelten *Xenopus*—Beinen," *Rev. Suisse Zool.,* **58**: 391–398.

BRUNST, V. V., 1950. "Influence of x-rays on limb regeneration in urodele amphibians," *Quart. Rev. Biol.,* **25**: 1–29.

BUTLER, E. G., 1933. "The effects of x-radiation on the regeneration of the forelimbs of *Amblystoma* larvae," *J. Exp. Zool.,* **65**: 271–315.

————, 1935. "Studies on limb regeneration in x-rayed *Amblystoma* larvae," *Anat. Record,* **62**: 295–307.

————, and H. F. BLUM, 1963. "Supernumerary limbs of urodele larvae resulting from localized ultraviolet light," *Develop. Biol.,* **7**: 218–233.

————, and J. P. O'BRIEN, 1942. "Effects of localized X-irradiation on regeneration of the urodele limb," *Anat. Record,* **84**: 407–413.

———, and O. E. SCHOTTÉ, 1949. "Effects of delayed denervation on regenerative activity in limbs of urodele larvae," *J. Exp. Zool.*, 112: 361–392.

———, and M. B. WARD, 1965. "Reconstitution of the spinal cord following ablation in urodele larvae," *J. Exp. Zool.*, 160: 47–66.

CHALKLEY, D. T., 1959. "The cellular basis of limb regeneration." In *Regeneration in vertebrates*, ed. by C. S. Thornton. Chicago: University of Chicago Press, pp. 34–58.

COULOMBRE, J. L., and A. J. COULOMBRE, 1965. "Regeneration of the neural retina in the chick embryo," *Develop. Biol.*, 12: 79–92.

DAS, N. K., and M. ALFERT, 1961. "Accelerated DNA synthesis in onion root meristem during x-irradiation," *Proc. Nat. Acad. Sci. U. S.*, 47: 1–6.

DECK, J. D., 1955. "The innervation of urodele limbs of reversed proximodistal polarity," *J. Morphol.*, 96: 301–331.

DENT, J. N., 1962. "Limb regeneration in larvae and metamorphosing individuals of the South African clawed toad," *J. Morphol.*, 110: 61–78.

FABER, J., 1962. "A threshold effect on the morphogenetic realization of transplanted limb regenerates of *Ambystoma mexicanum*," *Arch. Biol.*, 73: 379–403.

FREEMAN, G., 1963. "Lens regeneration from the cornea in *Xenopus laevis*," *J. Exp. Zool.*, 154: 39–65.

GLADE, R. W., 1963. "Effects of tail skin, epidermis, and dermis on limb regeneration in *Triturus viridescens* and *Siredon mexicanum*," *J. Exp. Zool.*, 152: 169–193.

GOSS, R. J., 1956. "An experimental analysis of taste barbel regeneration in the catfish," *J. Exp. Zool.*, 131: 27–50.

———, 1961. "Regeneration of vertebrate appendages." In *Advances in morphogenesis*, Vol. 1, ed. by M. Abercrombie and J. Brachet. New York: Academic Press, Inc., pp. 103–152.

———, 1964. *Adaptive growth*. New York: Academic Press, Inc.

GROBSTEIN, C., 1947. "The role of androgen in declining regenerative capacity during morphogenesis of the *Platypoecilus maculatus* gonopodium," *J. Exp. Zool.*, 106: 313–344.

GROSS, J., 1964. "Studies on the biology of connective tissue. Remodeling of collagen in metamorphosis," *Medicine*, 43: 291–303.

HAAS, H. J., 1962. "Studies on the mechanisms of joint and bone formation in the skeleton rays of fish fins," *Develop. Biol.*, 5: 1–34.

HAY, E. D., 1956. "Effects of thyroxine on limb regeneration in the newt, *Triturus viridescens*," *Bull. Johns Hopkins Hosp.*, 99: 262–285.

———, 1959. "Electron microscopic observations of muscle dedifferentiation in regenerating *Amblystoma* limbs," *Develop. Biol.*, 1: 555–585.

———, 1962. "Cytological studies of dedifferentiation and differentiation in regenerating amphibian limbs." In *Regeneration*, ed. by D. Rudnick. New York: The Ronald Press Co., pp. 177–210.

————, and D. A. Fischman, 1961. "Origin of the blastema in regenerating limbs of the newt *Triturus viridescens*," *Develop. Biol.*, 3: 26–59.

Holtzer, H., 1959. "The development of mesodermal axial structures in regeneration and embryogenesis." In *Regeneration in vertebrates*, ed. by C. S. Thornton. Chicago: University of Chicago Press, pp. 15–33.

Humphrey, R. R., 1966. "A recessive factor (o, for ova deficient) determining a complex of abnormalities in the Mexican axolotl *(Ambystoma mexicanum)*," *Develop. Biol.*, 13: 57–76.

Ide-Rozas, A., 1936. "Die Cytologischen Verhatinisse bei der Regeneration von Kaselquappenextremitaten," *Arch. Entwicklungsmech. Or.*, 135: 552–608.

Johnson, E. A., and M. Singer, 1964. "A histochemical study of succinic and lactic dehydrogenases in the regenerating forelimb of the adult newt, *Triturus*," *Proc. Soc. Exp. Biol. Med.*, 117: 27–31.

Kamrin, R. P., and M. Singer, 1955. "The influence of the spinal cord in regeneration of the tail of the lizard, *Anolis carolinensis*," *J. Exp. Zool.*, 128: 611–628.

Karasaki, S., 1964. "An electron microscopic study of Wolffian lens regeneration in the adult newt," *J. Ultrastruct. Res.*, 11: 246–273.

Kiortsis, V., and H. A. L. Trampusch, 1965. *Regeneration in animals and related problems.* Amsterdam, Netherlands: North-Holland Publishing Co.

Korschelt, E., 1927. *Regeneration und Transplantation. Band I, Regeneration.* Berlin: Verlag von Gebrüder Borntraeger.

Lillie, F. R., and M. Juhn, 1932. "The physiology of development of feathers. I. Growth-rate and pattern in the individual feather," *Physiol. Zool.*, 5: 124–184.

Moffat, L. A., and A. D'A. Bellairs, 1964. "The regenerative capacity of the tail in embryonic and post-natal lizards *(Lacerta vivipara Jacquin)*," *J. Embryol. Exp. Morphol.*, 12: 769–786.

Needham, J., 1962. *Biochemistry and morphogenesis.* New York: Cambridge University Press.

Niazi, I. A., 1964. "Effect of destruction of the notochord in the stump on tail regeneration in the ammocoetes," *Canad. J. Zool.*, 42: 707–714.

Nicholas, J., 1955. "Regeneration. Vertebrates." In *Analysis of development* ed. by B. H. Willier, P. A. Weiss, and V. Hamburger. Philadelphia: W. B. Saunders Co., pp. 674–698.

O'Steen, W. K., 1958. "Regeneration of the intestine in adult urodeles," *J. Morphol.*, 103: 435–478.

————, 1959. "Regeneration and repair of the intestine in *Rana clamitans* larvae," *J. Exp. Zool.*, 141: 449–476.

————, and B. E. Walker, 1962. "Radioautographic studies of regeneration in the common newt. III. Regeneration and repair of the intestine," *Anat. Record,* **142:** 179–188.

Overton, J., 1965. "Changes in cell fine structure during lens regeneration in *Xenopus laevis*," *J. Cell Biol.,* **24:** 211–222.

Parker, G. H., 1932. "On the trophic impulse, so called, its rate and nature," *Am. Naturalist.,* **66:** 147–158.

Peadon, A. M., and M. Singer, 1965. "A quantitative study of forelimb innervation in relation to regenerative capacity in the larval, land stage, and adult forms of *Triturus viridescens*," *J. Exp. Zool.,* **159:** 337–346.

Piatt, J., 1955. "Regeneration of the spinal cord in the salamander," *J. Exp. Zool.,* **129:** 177–208.

Polezhayev, L. W., 1945. *Fundamentals of physiology of development of the vertebrates* (in Russian). Moscow and Leningrad: Acad. Sci. U. S. S. R.

————, 1946. "The loss and restoration of regenerative capacity in the limbs of tailless amphibia," *Biol. Rev.,* **21:** 141–147.

Reyer, R. W., 1954. "Regeneration of the lens in the amphibian eye," *Quart. Rev. Biol.,* **29:** 1–46.

————, 1962. "Regeneration in the amphibian eye." In *Regeneration,* ed. by D. Rudnick. New York: The Ronald Press Co., pp. 211–265.

Rose, S. M., 1944. "Methods of initiating limb regeneration in adult Anura," *J. Exp. Zool.,* **95:** 149–170.

————, 1948. "Epidermal dedifferentiation during blastema formation in regenerating limbs of *Triturus viridescens*," *J. Exp. Zool.,* **108:** 337–361.

————, 1964. "Regeneration." In *Physiology of the amphibia,* ed. by J. A. Moore. New York: Academic Press, Inc., pp. 545–622.

Ruben, L. N., and M. Ball, 1964. "The implantation of lymphosarcoma of *Xenopus laevis* into regenerating and non-regenerating forelimbs of that species," *J. Morphol.,* **115,** 225–238.

Salpeter, M. M., 1965. "Disposition of nerve fibers in the regenerating limb of the adult newt, *Triturus*," *J. Morphol.,* **117:** 201–212.

Scharf, A., 1961. "Experiments on regenerating rat digits," *Growth,* **25:** 7–23.

Scheuing, M. R., and M. Singer, 1957. "The effects of microquantities of beryllium ion on the regenerating forelimb of the adult newt, *Triturus*," *J. Exp. Zool.,* **136:** 301–328.

Schmidt, A. J., and M. Weary, 1963. "Localization of acid phosphatase in the regenerating forelimb of the adult newt, *Diemictylus viridescens*," *J. Exp. Zool.,* **152:** 101–114.

Schotté, O. E., 1961. "Systemic factors in initiation of regenerative processes in limbs of larval and adult salamanders." In *Molecular and cellular synthesis,* ed. by D. Rudnick. New York: The Ronald Press Co., pp. 161–192.

————, and E. G. Butler, 1944. "Phases in regeneration of the urodele limb and their dependence upon the nervous system," *J. Exp. Zool.,* **97:** 95–121.

————, and A. B. HALL, 1952. "Effects of hypophysectomy upon phases of regeneration in progress (*Triturus viridescens*)," *J. Exp. Zool.*, **121**: 521–560.

————, and M. HARLAND, 1943. "Amputation level and regeneration in limbs of late *Rana clamitans* tadpoles," *J. Morphol.*, **73**: 329–361.

————, and C. B. SMITH, 1959. "Wound healing processes in amputated mouse digits," *Biol. Bull.*, **117**: 546–561.

————, and J. F. WILBER, 1958. "Effects of adrenal transplants upon forelimb regeneration in normal and in hypophysectomized frogs," *J. Embryol. Exp. Morphol.*, **6**: 247–261.

SIMPSON, S. B., JR., 1965. "Regeneration of the lizard tail." In *Regeneration in animals and related problems*, ed. by V. Kiortsis and H. A. L. Trampusch. Amsterdam, Netherlands: North-Holland Publishing Co., pp. 431–443.

SINGER, M., 1952. "The influence of the nerve in regeneration of the amphibian extremity," *Quart. Rev. Biol.*, **27**: 169–200.

————, 1954. "Induction of regeneration of the forelimb of the postmetamorphic frog by augmentation of the nerve supply," *J. Exp. Zool.*, **126**: 419–472.

————, 1960. "Nervous mechanisms in the regeneration of body parts in vertebrates." In *Developing cell systems and their control*, ed. by D. Rudnick. New York: The Ronald Press Co., pp. 115–133.

————, and L. CRAVEN, 1948. "The growth and morphogenesis of the regenerating forelimb of adult *Triturus* following denervation at various stages of development," *J. Exp. Zool.*, **108**: 279–308.

————, and S. INOUE, 1964. "The nerve and the epidermal apical cap in regeneration of the forelimb of adult *Triturus*," *J. Exp. Zool.*, **155**: 105–116.

————, and M. M. SALPETER, 1961. "Regeneration in vertebrates: the role of wound epithelium." In *Growth in living systems*, ed. by M. X. Zarrow. New York: Basic Books, Inc., pp. 277–311.

STEEN, T. P., and C. S. THORNTON, 1963. "Tissue interaction in amputated aneurogenic limbs of *Amblystoma* larvae," *J. Exp. Zool.*, **154**: 207–221.

STEVENS, J., L. N. RUBEN, D. LOCKWOOD, and H. ROSE, 1965. "Implant-induced accessory limbs in urodeles: fresh, frozen, and boiled tissues," *J. Morphol.*, **117**, 213–228.

STINSON, B. D., 1958. "Chemical enhancement of radioresistance in regenerating and developing limbs of urodele larvae," *J. Morphol.*, **103**: 387–434.

STONE, L. S., 1959. "Regeneration of the retina, iris and lens." In *Regeneration in vertebrates*, ed. by C. S. Thornton. Chicago: University of Chicago Press, pp. 3–14.

SZANTO, GY., 1961. *Regeneration and wound healing.* Budapest: Akadémiai Kiadó.

TAKATA, C., J. F. ALBRIGHT, and T. YAMADA, 1964. "Lens antigens in a lens-regenerating system studied by the immunofluorescent technique," *Develop. Biol.*, **9**: 385–397.

————, ————, and ————, 1965. "Lens fiber differentiation and gamma crystallins: immunofluorescent study of Wolffian regeneration," *Science*, **147**: 1299–1301.

THORNTON, C. S., 1938. "The histogenesis of muscle in the regenerating forelimb of larval *Amblystoma punctatum*," *J. Morphol.*, **62**: 17–47.

————, 1942. "Studies on the origin of the regeneration blastema in *Triturus viridescens,*" *J. Exp. Zool.,* **89:** 375–390.

————, 1960. "Influence of an eccentric epidermal cap on limb regeneration in *Amblystoma* larvae," *Develop. Biol.,* **2:** 551–569.

————, and D. W. Kraemer, 1951. "The effect of injury on denervated unamputated forelimbs of *Amblystoma* larvae," *J. Exp. Zool.,* **117:** 415–439.

————, and T. P. Steen, 1962. "Eccentric blastema formation in aneurogenic limbs of *Amblystoma* larvae following epidermal cap deviation," *Develop. Biol.,* **5:** 328–343.

Trampusch, H. A. L., 1959. "The effect of x-rays on regenerative capacity." In *Regeneration in vertebrates,* ed. by C. S. Thornton. Chicago: University of Chicago Press, pp. 83–98.

Van Stone, J. M., 1955. "The relationship between innervation and regenerative capacity in hind limbs of *Rana sylvatica,*" *J. Morphol.,* **97:** 345–392.

Weiss, P., 1939. *Principles of development.* New York: Holt, Rinehart and Winston, Inc.

Wilkerson, J. A., 1963. "The role of growth hormone in regeneration in the forelimb of the hypophysectomized newt," *J. Exp. Zool.,* **154:** 223–230.

Windle, W. F., 1955. *Regeneration in the central nervous system.* Springfield, Ill.: Charles C. Thomas, Publisher.

Woodland, W. N. F., 1920. "Some observations on caudal autotomy and regeneration in the gecko (*Hemidactylus flaviviridis,* Rupel) with notes on the tails of Sphenodon and Pygopus," *Quart. J. Microscop. Sci.,* **65:** 63–100.

Wolsky, A., and N. Van Doi, 1965. "The effects of actinomycin on regeneration processes in amphibians," *Trans. N.Y. Acad. Sci.,* Ser. II, **27:** 882–893.

Yamada, T., and C. Takata, 1963. "An autoradiographic study of protein synthesis in regenerative tissue transformation of iris into lens in the newt," *Develop. Biol.,* **8:** 358–369.

Yntema, C. L., 1959. "Blastema formation in sparsely innervated and aneurogenic forelimbs of *Amblystoma* larvae," *J. Exp. Zool.,* **142:** 423–439.

Zika, J., and M. Singer, 1965. "The relation between nerve fiber number and limb regenerative capacity in the lizard, *Anolis,*" *Anat. Record,* **152:** 137–140.

Chapter Three
Mammals

Arey, L. B., 1936. "Wound healing," *Physiol. Rev.,* **16:** 327–406.

Billingham, R. E., 1964. "Transplantation immunity and the maternal fetal relation (concluded)," *New Engl. J. Med.,* **270:** 720–725.

Bintliff, S., and B. E. Walker, 1960. "Radioautographic study of skeletal muscle regeneration," *Am. J. Anat.,* **106:** 233–265.

BUCHER, N. R. L., 1963. "Regeneration of mammalian liver," *Intern. Rev. Cytol,* 15: 245–300.

BURKE, J. F., L. V. LEAK, and P. J. MORRIS, 1966. "The function of lymphatic capillaries in normal and inflammatory states," *Am. J. Anat.,* on press.

CAMERON, I. L., and P. C. GREULICH, 1963. "Evidence for an essentially constant duration of DNA synthesis in renewing epithelia of the adult mouse," *J. Cell Biol.,* 18: 31–40.

CARTWRIGHT, G. E., J. W. ATHENS, and M. M. WINTROBE, 1964. "The kinetics of granulopoiesis in normal man," *Blood,* 24: 780–803.

CRONKITE, E. P., and T. M. FLIEDNER, 1964. "Granulocytopoiesis," *New Engl. J. Med.,* 270: 1347–1403.

DAWSON, A. B., 1940. "Cell division in relation to differentiation," *Growth Suppl.,* 91–106.

DUNPHY, J. E., and R. WARREN, 1963. "Wound healing." In *Surgery,* ed. by R. Warren. Philadelphia: W. B. Saunders Co., pp. 1–21.

EDDS, M. V., JR., 1953. "Collateral nerve regeneration," *Quart. Rev. Biol.,* 28: 260–276.

EDWARDS, L. C., and J. E. DUNPHY, 1958. "Wound healing. I. Injury and normal repair," *New Engl. J. Med.,* 259: 224–233.

ELKIND, M. M., A. HAN, and K. W. VOLZ, 1963. "Radiation response of mammalian cells grown in culture. IV. Dose dependence of division delay and post-irradiation growth of surviving and nonsurviving Chinese hamster cells," *J. Nat. Cancer Inst.,* 30: 705–721.

GALBRAITH, P. R., L. S. VALBERG, and M. BROWN, 1965. "Patterns of granulocyte kinetics in health, infection and carcinoma," *Blood,* 25: 683–692.

GELFANT, S., 1963. "A new theory on the mechanism of cell division." In *Cell growth and cell division,* ed. by R. J. C. Harris. New York: Academic Press, Inc., pp. 229–259.

GOSS, R. J., 1964a. "The role of skin in antler regeneration." In *Advances in biology of skin, Wound healing,* Vol. 5, ed. by W. Montagna and R. E. Billingham. New York: Pergamon Press, Inc., pp. 194–207.

———, 1964b. *Adaptive growth.* New York: Academic Press, Inc.

GRAHAM, C. F., and R. W. MORGAN, 1966. "Changes in the cell cycle during early amphibian development," *Develop. Biol.,* on press.

GRISHAM, J. W., 1962. "A morphologic study of DNA synthesis and cell proliferation in regenerating rat liver," *Cancer Res.,* 22: 842–849.

HAM, A. W., 1965. *Histology.* Philadelphia: J. B. Lippincott Co.

HARDING, C. V., and B. D. SRINIVASAN, 1961. "A propagated stimulation of DNA synthesis and cell division," *Exp. Cell Res.,* 25: 326–340.

HILD, W., and G. ZETLER, 1953. "Experimenteller Beweis für die Entstehung der sog. Hypophysenhinterlappenwirkstoffe im Hypothalamus," *Arch. Ges. Physiol.,* 257: 169–201.

Hsu, T. C., W. Schmid, and E. Stubblefield, 1964. "DNA replication sequences in higher animals." In *The role of chromosomes in development,* ed. by M. Locke. New York: Academic Press Inc., pp. 83–112.

Jackson, D. S., D. B. Flickinger, and J. E. Dunphy, 1960. Biochemical studies of connective tissue repair," *Ann. N. Y. Acad. Sci.,* **86:** 943–947.

James, D. W., 1964. "Wound contraction—a synthesis." In *Advances in biology of skin: Wound healing,* Vol. 5, ed. by W. Montagna and R. E. Billingham. New York: Pergamon Press, pp. 216–230.

Johnson, F. R., and R. M. H. McMinn, 1960. "The cytology of wound healing of body surfaces in mammals," *Biol. Rev.,* **35:** 364–412.

Jones, D. S., 1957. "Healing of muscle tissue." In *The healing of wounds: A symposium on recent trends and studies,* ed. by M. B. Williamson. New York: McGraw-Hill Book Co., Inc., pp. 149–167.

Lamerton, L. F., and R. J. M. Fry, 1963. *Cell proliferation.* Oxford: Basil Black-well & Mott, Ltd.

Lash, J. W., H. Holtzer, and H. Swift, 1957. "Regeneration of mature skeletal muscle," *Anat. Record,* **128:** 679–697.

Leblond, C. P., 1965. "The time dimension in histology," *Am. J. Anat.,* **116:** 1–27.

————, B. Messier, and B. Kopriwa, 1959. "Thymidine-H³ as a tool for the investigation of the renewal of cell populations," *Lab. Invest.,* **8:** 296–308.

Le Gros Clark, W. E., 1946. "An experimental study of regeneration of mammalian striped muscle," *J. Anat.,* **80:** 24–26.

Patt, H. M., and H. Quastler, 1963. "Radiation effects on cell renewal and related systems," *Physiol. Rev.,* **43:** 357–396.

Pietsch, P., 1961. "The effects of colchicine on regeneration of mouse skeletal muscle," *Anat. Record,* **139:** 167–172.

Prescott, D. M., 1964. "The normal cell cycle," In *Synchrony in cell division and growth,* ed. by E. Zeuthen. New York: Interscience Publishers, Inc., pp. 71–97.

Puck, T. T., and J. Steffen, 1963. "Life cycle analysis of mammalian cells. I. A method for localizing metabolic events within the life cycle, and its applica-tion to the action of colcemide and sublethal doses of X-irradiation," *Biophys. J.,* **3:** 379–397.

Quastler, H., and F. G. Sherman, 1959. "Cell population kinetics in the intestinal epithelium of the mouse," *Exp. Cell Res.,* **17:** 420–438.

Reiskin, A. B., and M. L. Mendelsohn, 1964. "A comparison of the cell cycle in induced carcinomas and their normal counterpart," *Cancer Res.,* **24:** 1131–1136.

Ross, R., 1964. "Collagen formation in healing wounds." In *Advances in biology of skin: Wound healing,* Vol. 5, ed. by W. Montagna and R. E. Billingham. New York: Pergamon Press, Inc., pp. 155–164.

RUSSELL, P. S., and A. P. MONACO, 1964. "The biology of tissue transplantation (concluded)," *New Engl. J. Med.,* **271**: 776–783.

SELYE H., and T. McKEOWN, 1934. "On the regenerative power of the uterus," *J. Anat.,* **69**: 79–81.

SHEA, S. M., 1964. "Kinetics of hepatocyte proliferation in the early stages of liver regeneration," *Exp. Cell Res.,* **36**: 325–334.

SPERRY, R. W., 1959. "The growth of nerve circuits," *Sci. Am.,* **201**: 68–75.

WASHBURN, W. N., 1955. "Comparative histochemical observations of wound healing in adult rats and cultured human epithelium. III. Alkaline and acid phosphatase," *J. Invest. Dermatol.,* **24**: 537–544.

WATTS, G. T., H. C. GRILLO, and J. GROSS, 1958. "Studies in wound healing. II. The role of granulation tissue in contraction," *Ann. Surg.,* **148**: 153–160.

WEISS, P., 1955. "Special vertebrate organogenesis: nervous system." In *Analysis of development,* ed. by B. H. Willier, P. A. Weiss, and V. Hamburger. Philadelphia: W. B. Saunders Co., pp. 346–401.

——, and H. B. HISCOE, 1948. "Experiments on the mechanism of nerve growth," *J. Exp. Zool.,* **107**: 315–396.

Chapter Four
Fine Structure of Regeneration Cells

BEN-OR, S., and E. BELL, 1965. "Skin antigens in the chick embryo in relation to other developmental events," *Develop. Biol.,* **11**: 184–201.

BODEMER, C. W., 1962. "Distribution of ribonucleic acid in the regenerating urodele limb as determined by autoradiographic localization of uridine-H^3," *Anat. Rec.,* **142**: 457–467.

BRIGGS, R., and T. J. KING, 1959. "Nucleocytoplasmic interactions in eggs and embryos." In *The cell,* Vol. 1, ed. by J. Brachet and A. E. Mirsky. New York: Academic Press, Inc., pp. 537–617.

BROWN, D. D., 1965. "RNA synthesis during early development." In *Developmental and metabolic control mechanisms and neoplasms,* ed. by R. L. Clark. Baltimore: Williams and Wilkins Co., pp. 219–234.

CARO, L. G., and G. E. PALADE, 1964. "Protein synthesis, storage and discharge in the pancreatic acinar cell. An autoradiographic study," *J. Cell Biol.,* **20**: 473–495.

DAWSON, A. B., 1940. "Cell division in relation to differentiation," *Growth Suppl.,* pp. 91–106.

FAWCETT, D. W., 1966. *The cell—Its organelles and inclusions.* Philadelphia: W. B. Saunders Co.

Grobstein, C., 1959. "Differentiation of vertebrate cells." In *The cell*, Vol. 1, ed. by J. Brachet and A. E. Mîrsky. New York: Academic Press, Inc., pp. 437–496.

Gurdon, J. B., 1962. "The developmental capacity of nuclei taken from intestinal epithelial cells of feeding tadpoles," *J. Embryol. Exp. Morphol.*, 10: 622–640.

———, 1964. "The transplantation of living cell nuclei." In *Advances in morphogenesis*, Vol. 4, ed. by M. Abercrombie and J. Brachet. New York: Academic Press, Inc., pp. 1–43.

———, and D. D. Brown, 1965. "Cytoplasmic regulation of RNA synthesis and nucleolus formation in developing embryos of Xenopus laevis," *J. Mol. Biol.*, 12: 27–35.

Harrison, R. G, 1933. "Some difficulties of the determination problem," *Am. Naturalist*, 67: 306–321.

Hay, E. D., 1958. "The fine structure of blastema cells and differentiating cartilage cells in regenerating limbs of Amblystoma larvae," *J. Biophys. Biochem. Cytol.*, 4: 583–592.

———, 1963. "The fine structure of differentiating muscle in the salamander tail," *Z. Zellforsch.*, 59: 6–34.

———, 1965. "Limb development and regeneration." In *Organogenesis*, ed. by R. L. DeHaan and H. Ursprung. New York: Holt, Rinehart and Winston, Inc., pp. 315–336.

———, and J. P. Revel, 1963. "The fine structure of the DNP component of the nucleus," *J. Cell Biol.*, 16: 29–51.

Holtzer, H., 1963. "Mitosis and cell transformations." In *General physiology of cell specialization*, ed. by D. Mazia and A. Tyler. New York: McGraw-Hill Book Co., pp. 80–90.

Konigsberg, I. R., 1965. "Aspects of cytodifferentiation of skeletal muscle." In *Organogenesis*, ed. by R. L. DeHaan and H. Ursprung. New York: Holt, Rinehart and Winston, Inc., pp. 337–358.

———, and S. H. Hauschka, 1965. "Cell and tissue interactions in the reproduction of cell type." In *Reproduction: Molecular, subcellular and cellular*, ed. by M. Locke. New York: Academic Press, Inc., pp. 243–290.

Pedersen, K. J., 1959. "Cytological studies on the planarian neoblast," *Z. Zellforsch.*, 50: 799–817.

Peterson, M., and C. P. Leblond, 1964. "Synthesis of complex carbohydrates in the Golgi region, as shown by radioautography after injection of labeled glucose," *J. Cell Biol.*, 21: 143–148.

Porter, K. R., 1964. "Cell fine structure and biosynthesis of intercellular macromolecules," *Biophys. J.*, 4: 167–196.

Revel, J. P., 1964. "A stain for the ultrastructural localization of acid mucopolysaccharides," *J. Microscop.*, 3: 535–544.

————, and E. D. HAY, 1963. "An autoradiographic and electron microscopic study of collagen synthesis in differentiating cartilage," *Z. Zellforsch.*, **61:** 110–144.

RUTHMAN, A., 1965. "The fine structure of RNA-storing archaeocytes from gemmules of fresh-water sponges," *Quart. J. Microscop. Sci.*, **106:** 99–114.

SALPETER, M. M., and L. BACHMANN, 1964. "Autoradiography with the electron microscope. I. A procedure for improving resolution, sensitivity, and contrast," *J. Cell. Biol.*, **22:** 469–476.

————, and M. SINGER, 1960. "The fine structure of mesenchymatous cells in the regenerating forelimb of the adult newt, *Triturus*," *Develop. Biol.*, **2:** 516–534.

————, and ————, 1962. "The fine structure of mesenchymatous cells in regenerating limbs of larval and adult *Triturus*." In *Electron microscopy*, Vol. 2, ed. by S. S. Breese. New York: Academic Press, Inc., p. OO–12.

SIEKEVITZ, P., and G. E. PALADE, 1960. "A cytochemical study on the pancreas of the guinea pig. V. In vivo incorporation of leucine-1-C^{14} into the chymotrypsinogen of various cell fractions," *J. Biophys. Biochem. Cytol.*, **7:** 619–630.

SLAUTTERBACK, D. B., and D. W. FAWCETT, 1959. "The development of the cnidoblasts of *Hydra*. An electron microscope study of cell differentiation," *J. Biophys. Biochem. Cytol.*, **5:** 441–452.

SPEMANN, H., 1938. *Embryonic development and induction*. New Haven, Conn.: Yale University Press.

STEWARD, F. C., 1963. "The control of growth in plant cells," *Sci. Am.*, **209:** 104–113.

SWANN, N. M., 1958. "The control of cell division. A review. II. Special mechanisms," *Cancer Res.*, **18:** 1118–1160.

THORNTON, C. R., 1938. "The histogenesis of the regenerating forelimb of larval *Amblystoma* after exarticulation of the humerus." *J. Morphol.*, **62:** 219–242.

WADDINGTON, C. H., and M. M. PERRY, 1963. "Helical arrangements of ribosomes in differentiating muscle cells," *Exp. Cell Res.*, **30:** 599–600.

WATSON, J. D., 1965. *Molecular biology of the gene*. New York W. A. Benjamin, Inc.

WEISS, P., 1950. "Perspectives in the field of morphogenesis," *Quart. Rev. Biol.*, **25:** 177–198.

WESSELS, N. K., 1965. "Morphology and proliferation during early feather development," *Develop. Biol.*, **12:** 151–153.

indexes

name index

subject index

Acellular perisarc, 18, 19
Acoela, 26
Acoelomate animals, 1–5
    reproduction among, 5–10
Acriflavine, 13
ACTH, 71, 77, 93, 94
Amaroecium, 39
Ambystoma, 43, 50, 55, 56, 57,
    61, 66, 67, 70, 71, 73, 99–
    100, 101
Ambystomidae, 48
Ammocoetes, 41
Amoeba, 5
Amphibians, evolution of regen-
    eration in, 41–47
Amphioxus (*see* Cephalochor-
    data)
Annelids, 4, 5, 26–32
Anolis carolinensis, 77
Antennae, regeneration of, 32–
    34
Anthozoa, 2, 16
Anurans, 42, 43, 48, 52, 75, 76
Apical epithelium, 6, 8, 64–71
Arbacia, 35
Archaeocytes, 3, 6, 14, 15, 16
    fine structure of, 110
Arthropods, 4, 5, 32–34
Ascidians, 10, 11, 36–40
Asexual reproduction, modes of,
    5, 6
    in coelenterates, 6–9

in oligochaetes, 28
in polychaetes, 28, 29
in protozoans, 5, 7
in sponges, 5, 6
in tunicates, 10, 11, 36–40
See also Regeneration
Atrial epithelium, 10, 11, 36
Aurelia, 18
Autolytus, 28, 29, 30, 31
Autotomy, 34, 45
Axolotl, 43
Axons, growth rate of, 89, 90

Bacteriostatic agents, 13
Beryllium, 75
Binary fission (*see* Fission)
Bio-electrical fields, 20, 30, 54
Birds, 42, 45, 52, 53, 116
Blastema, 54-64, 105–107, 117,
    118
Blood, renewal of, 82, 83
Blood cells, 37, 57, 82, 83
Bone fractures, 86, 87
Bone marrow, 82, 83
Botryllus, 10, 11, 36, 37
Bryozoa (*see* Ectoprocta, Ento-
    procta)
Budding, 5, 6
    in coelenterates, 6–9
    in sponges, 5
    in tunicates, 10, 11, 36–40
Bursaria, 12, 13

141